FOLLOW THE RIVER

Jerry McGee

Esjay Press   Keizer, Oregon

ESJAY PRESS
4310 Shoreline Dr. N.
Keizer, Oregon 97303

ISBN: 0-9672772-1-3

Library of Congress Control Number: 2001098794

First Edition

Cover design by Bruce DeRoos

Book design and Layout by DIMI PRESS

Printed in 12pt Palatino

Dedicated to
The Charter Members of the Clark Co.
Search and Rescue
and to Wesley Jordan

Credits and Acknowledgments

Evelyn Hoxsey, cover painting
Robert and Jane Roach, technical advisors
Norma Benson, technical adviser
Gene Hoxsey, technical advisor

Contents

Author's Note

I have taken editorial license with the diary we discovered. For example, I have added chapter titles which, of course, were not in the diary. I have guessed at some of the words that were scratched out or too blurred to read. In addition in many cases I have changed a narrative account into a dialogue.

Chapter 1

The Discovery

October 1990

The rain continued to pour steadily. A herd of elk with any self-respect would have bedded down for the night. If we had any sense, I thought, we should do the same. A wet night out for us was already a guarantee. But that's O.K., we're well equipped. It was too bad though that our sense of direction didn't match the quality of our gear. We were not lost—just a bit confused.

If this notebook is found, please see that my mother gets it. Her name and telephone number are in the back. We think it is the Fourth of July. I hope this will prove to be our

Independence Day. The plan is to go downstream when we leave. I will leave a note at Camp #1 and at each succeeding camp.

We will follow the river until we find civilization or the ocean. The Monkey thinks it is about fifty miles to the coast. If we reach the coast and still have not met anyone we will turn south and follow the coastline. We will walk all the way to Vancouver if we have to, but we are going to make it out. We have gone through too much not to make it now.

We will make it out—but in case we don't, my mother would want this diary.

Thank you,
SS

"Hey, come over here and look at this. Something is strange," Bill said. Bill was one of my hunting buddies. "Looks like the wreckage of a plane," he said.

"I think you are right," I said, without looking up. The others had started to gather down the hill from the rock bench where I had found some cover from the rain.

"Is there anyone alive?" A latecomer asked.

"Are you kidding? This is an old crash, at least seven or eight years old, judging by the growth over it."

"No," I said, "not that old. The crash occurred the last week of September."

"You mean only a month ago?" Bill was doubtful.

"No, not last month," I said. "The crash happened September 22, 1986 over four years ago."

"How in the hell do you know that?" he asked. I didn't have to answer. By this time the black spiral notebook from which I was reading, was apparent to everyone.

"My God, a diary," Butch said, as he pushed closer.

"A diary, or a log, or at least some kind of written account," I said.

Hunters are not known for their quietness, but the only sound we heard was the tattoo of the rain on the fallen maple leaves. The rain ,if anything, had increased.

"Tether the nags below that rock bench. That looks like as good a place as any to hole up for the night," Jack, our guide, had interrupted our attention to the book. I slipped the book inside my shirt to protect it from the rain.

We all shuffled in single file toward the rock outcropping that Jack had pointed out. On the way past the wreckage of the plane, Jack slid off his horse and stood for a moment beside a mound of rocks. We turned in our saddles to watch. He reached over and picked up a cross fashioned of limbs and bound together by some rusted wire. He righted the cross and wedged it between two rocks.

"We will do a better job on this in the morning," he said.

We were tired, but there was an air of excitement and expectation that caused us to attend to the horses faster than normal in spite of the miserable conditions.

The first chore is always to start a fire. To start a fire in the open could take an hour or more and then another hour before one gets much real warmth from it. In this case, thanks to an unknown predecessor at this cave-like shelter, we had a good fire going within minutes.

In the center of a circle of rocks, which had been used as a fire pit, was tinder for a fire already laid out. Next to that was a pile of dry moss and a rick of dry wood.

Butch said,"Holy cow, he even laid a fire for us."

"There were two of them that survived,"I explained. I had the diary open and tipped toward the light from the fire.

"A boy and a girl survived. The boy was hurt in the crash," I said,"Let's break out the grub and I will read some more after we have eaten. If you are interested," I said.

"Eat? Like hell. We will eat when I say we eat. I'm the guide here." Jack spoke for everybody.

"Who's hungry?"and "Keep reading!"they all chorused. We all were curious about the contents of the diary. I had to smile to myself because these were the same people who I had heard grouse for the last two hours about how hungry they were.

I turned to get more light on the pages. The writing was faint at best, and often smeared or fuzzy.

I began to read aloud and deliberately to our subdued group of elk hunters.

*   *   *   *   *   *

The fire had been restoked many times from the pile of wood that had been left for use With the assistance of three others reading in relay, and after several hours, the book was finally back to me to finish.

It was one o'clock in the morning, and except for chewing on some Smoke Craft Jerky we still had not eaten. I finished the diary and set the book aside. One by one the men slid into their sleeping bags. No "final" words,were spoken. Words were not necessary. We had shared many thoughts throughout the late evening and early morning on what we were reading and hearing: disbelief, joy, fear, and the full range of emotions. At one point the book was given on to the next reader because eyes had become too blurred by moisture to read further.

My last thoughts before sleep rushed over me was that we must remember to replace the supply of wood before we go and that we would want to verify this story. This would be possible to do, I hoped in the morning light.

I can only wonder what the first night must have been like for those folks.

Chapter 2

The Crash

September 22, 1986

I am soaked through to the skin and cannot stop the spasms of shivering. The pilot is dead. I start to cry, not for him, but for myself. Why did this happen to me? Stupid, macho pilot. If he hadn't been such a hot dog, and thought more about flying the damn plane, this wouldn't have happened. And if he hadn't been so interested in setting up a big date with me, he would not have gotten us lost.

"Stupid. Stupid," I said out loud.

"If you're talking to him, he ain't listening. If you're talking to me save your breath."

I had forgotten that we had a kid passenger in the jump seat. I couldn't say that I liked the tone of his voice, but it *was* a voice.

"How could he have gotten lost?" I asked.

"If you had let the guy fly the plane...." he didn't complete his thought.

"Oh, so now this is all my fault some how," I

said. I started sobbing again and I didn't want to. I hurt all over. I cradled my lighter from the rain and the wind and lit up a cigarette.

"How about borrowing your lighter and your pack of smokes?" he said. With my best sarcasm I replied," Are you old enough to be smoking?"

I tossed first the pack and then the lighter to him.

I decided I would ignore the little bastard while I tried to think what to do. After a few minutes, however, I noticed that he had not lit up yet.

"I will take my cigarettes back now," I said.

"I threw them in the creek," he said, with a nod of his head toward the direction of the running water. I could not believe what I heard. A quick glance at the creek confirmed his crime. I saw the green and white cigarette package dance into the first ripple on its way to Japan.

"You son of a bitch. That was just plain mean."

"Not meant to be mean," he said, "just smart." He was calm and under control, but I was not. I waited, but he was not going to offer any further explanation.

"You did that on purpose, didn't you." I was shouting at him now.

"Yes, I did. That lighter has just so many flicks in it, and I don't want them wasted on your smoking," he said. "Do you get it?" He was still so damn calm. He went on, "This lighter may be the only thing of value that you have right now. It could mean life or death to us. Only I need to tell you that it is my lighter now, and you would have to kill me to get it back."

By God I think he means it. The look in his eyes

startled me. I felt compelled to say something because I had lost the control here; however, what I said was under my breath and not loud enough for him to hear. "You little monkey, when I want the lighter, I will sit on you and take it." I was still searching for an adequate comeback that I could say out loud and with force, when I noticed for the first time that something about him was not right. It was the way he was sprawled or something.

"Are you O.K. ?" I asked. He looked like he was about to say something but suddenly the color left his face and he slid sideways from his propped-up position. He was obviously injured but so far he had not murmured so much as a peep about it.

"My God, don't die on me, don't die on me," I said. I closed the fifteen feet or so that separated us. He had lost consciousness, but he was still alive. My first thought was that he had a head injury. I tried to sit him back up. I could see there was something wrong with his legs. By God, he was a tough kid. I had to give him that. At least I didn't have anything broken. He groaned but his eyes did not open. By compulsion I reached for a cigarette.

"Damn him for throwing them away," I said. "What am I going to do now?" The situation was bad enough without having this broken-up kid along for baggage.

"Damn it, what am I going to do now?" I repeated.

"What are you going to do now?" he asked, exhaling.

I was startled by his voice. I had not expected an answer.

"What *are* you going to do now?" he said. "You
are going to do what I tell you to do, Sister, because
if you do, you might live. That way I might live too.
Now, go down by the beaver dam—the dam, the
pond. See the pond?"

I hadn't noticed a pond, let alone a beaver dam.
Anyway it looked like a pile of brush to me.

"You will find dead sticks that you can pull
lengthwise from the dam," he said. "I need good
limbs. Don't bring back any twigs. I want heavy
duty sticks."

My look gave away my lack of comprehension.

"Two are for splints," he said, "the third one will
be a crutch, I hope."

I hesitated, just to collect myself, but he misin-
terpreted my hesitation.

"You will have to do as I say. That is the last time
I am going to tell you. I just don't have the time to
explain everything to you."

He seemed very tired. I could establish control
later. For now, I decided I had better do what he says.
I turned to dash down the bank to the pile of brush
where he had indicated, but he shot out his hand
and grabbed me hard by the arm.

"Slow, Sister, slow. Pick your way. This leg will
stay broken for a long time. It will only complicate
things if you stumble and fall," he said.

All kinds of thoughts raced through my mind as
I forced myself to go slow and deliberately. The little
Monkey made sense. *He is totally unlikeable. He must
be in terrible pain. He is strong.* I could still feel his
grip on my arm. I was amazed at how strong he was
for such a skinny kid.

I found the sticks that I hoped would satisfy him. I returned at a fast but careful pace, over the wet and slippery terrain. It would help if the rain would just stop.

He had propped himself up again into a sitting position.

"Only my left leg is broken, but I can't bear any weight on my right leg either. I don't think it is broken though," he said. He had his belt off and cinched a stick to either side of his left leg between the ankle and knee. He tore the sleeve off his denim shirt and tied it midway between his knee and thigh. He worked without a sound or any indication of pain, but I knew he was in torment.

His leg was swollen and the pant leg of his jeans was tight. He popped open the most wicked-looking folding knife that I have ever seen. With one motion, he slit his jeans leg from hip to cuff.

"My God, your leg is a mess," I said. I wished I hadn't said it quite like that, but he paid no attention. I was struck by how smooth his leg is. I wished mine were that smooth.

The exertion was almost too much for him. Still, no tears or other outward signs of pain. In an awkward span of silence, I wondered what time it was and glanced at my wrist where my watch should have been.

"It's about two o'clock," he said.

"How do you know that?"

"What difference does it make how I know it?" he said. "What does make a difference is that there are less than five hours of daylight left, and we have lots to do if we are going to see tomorrow."

"O.K. Monkey, what do you suggest?" That was the first time I called him "Monkey" to his face. It just came out. He didn't appear to notice.

"Four things," he said, "and in this order. First, we must get out of this rain, find cover, build a fire, get as dry as we can, and get something over us for the night." He clicked it off like he had drilled it a thousand times.

"Is that all the first thing?" I said.

"No, that's it," he said.

"That's five things, and anyway, what do you mean, for the night? If you think I'm sleeping out here tonight--could there be animals around here?"I hadn't thought about that prospect, and I wished I had thought of something else instead.

"I don't see that you have much choice about staying the night," he said. "But you will be lucky if you get any sleep. As for the wild animals, there are only little lions, and tigers and bears."

"I just asked. You don't have to be such a smart-ass," I said. He ignored my comment.

He said, "That old-growth windthrow is our best bet for a shelter." He pointed at a huge log on the ground which had been overturned in some ancient storm. "I am sorry to have to ask you to help me, but I can't walk or crawl," he said. "I am afraid I will displace the broken bone in my leg if I try. I wouldn't ask you if I thought I could move on my own," he said.

He sounded apologetic. The temptation to even the score was too great.

"Sure, I will help you. What are friends for?" I mocked. Either he didn't recognize my mockery, or he chose to ignore me once again. In any case, most

of the fun was taken out of my clever comment.
By the time I had dragged him the thirty yards
or so to the uprooted tree, I was exhausted, and I
am sure he was too. But he started at once to scoop
out a hollow in the soft soil under the side of the
root deep enough for him to sit upright. I stood in
the rain, not knowing what else to do.

"I will scoop you a dig, Sister, and you pull out
some of that moss you see under the log," he said.

I pulled at what I thought was a giant mound of
moss. I was surprised at how dry the moss was.

"Not nearly enough," he said.

This was his verbal reward for my efforts. He
had scooped out a hole for me which was close to
his but at a slight angle. Again, I didn't know what
to do, so I just watched him. With his knife he made
a pile of shavings from a dry stick. He placed a layer
of moss just inside the rain line under the overhang
of the log. Every movement was painful to him. He
made a little tepee of the shavings, and with great
deliberateness and care, he struck the lighter once.
The lighter, which he had stolen from me, worked. I
was amazed to see the moss catch and start to glow.
He added some more shavings, then some more
moss, a small piece of dry bark, a slab of bark, and
we had a fire.

"I am truly impressed," I said. I didn't feel as
tired now as the little fire gathered life.

"Now get us some limbs as dry as you can find,"
he said. "The end of this old fir tree would be a good
place to look."

"I thought I would dry myself off if you don't
mind," I said.

"Well, I do mind," he said. "The fuel is out there, not under here. We need lots of wood and you now only have about an hour of light left. You can get dry later."

On my fourth trip with limbs he stopped me.

"Over there is a dead cedar tree," he said. "I want you to pull the loose bark off and bring it here. The bark should peel easily. Get the strips as long as you can, OK.? Do you know which tree is the cedar tree?" he asked.

"Well, I am not stupid you know," I said. Fortunately, I had followed his line of sight, or I would have started off in the wrong direction. How did he expect me to know all this stuff? A tree is a tree.

I assumed that the strips were for the fire. I was wrong. The Monkey had his knife at work splitting the bark into long, inch-wide strips. Two limb-gathering trips later, I stole a look at his activities.

"You are weaving a blanket. Will it work?" I asked.

He knew my question was sincere and he seemed pleased with my observation and interest.

"It won't be any goose-feather job," he said, "but you will be surprised at how much body heat a woven cedar blanket will retain. If I cover the blanket with leaves and forest duff it will be even warmer."

"I'm impressed," I said. "How did you come up with that idea? Were you some kind of Boy Scout, or did you read it somewhere?"

There was a noticeable hesitation before his reply.

"I have never been a Boy Scout, and I can't read. I have done this before. I didn't just think it up," he said. "We need more wood. I will have a cover for both of us by the time you make a few more trips."

Perhaps, what he meant was that he just didn't read, but then I had the feeling that he said it the way it is, that he can't read. *Isn't that interesting? I could tell it was a sensitive area.* No need to explore that any more for now.

"That should do it for tonight," he said.

"At last the slave driver will let me stop packing wood," I said. In a short time I was warm and had actually started to dry out. *God, I am hungry, but I am not going to be the first to mention food. He has to be just as hungry as I am. Let him complain first.*

"If you are pretty dry, get covered up and try to sleep," he said. "Only don't get your blanket too close to the fire or you will go up like a Christmas tree."

He rolled over as if he had gone to sleep, but I knew he wasn't asleep. In any case the conversation was over for the night. Not that I minded.

God, what I wouldn't give for a cigarette right now. Maybe in the morning I can go downstream and look to see if the pack could have gotten hung up somewhere. I sure hope there is a smoker in the rescue party.

I woke up twice to hear the continued symphony of rain on dead leaves. Each time I stirred I noticed the fire was burning brightly. The Monkey must have been feeding it regularly. *Why shouldn't he? He ought to do something.*

So passed my first night somewhere in the Coast Range of British Columbia.

Chapter 3

No Sign Of Rescue

September 25th.

Y ou could say that I have had better days than the last four. *I am really concerned about the kid. He may be tough but he has* endured far too much. His legs are black. Not black and blue, just black. I have thought about gangrene, but I don't know what to look for, or what to do if it is gangrene. He has been running a fever for three days and he has been out of it most of the time. That is probably just as well.

I have tried to keep his handkerchief wet for his fore-head, and that seems to help some. I should elevate his legs but the quarters are too cramped to do that very well. I have loosened the bindings on his splints several times. I wish I knew more what to do.

It takes all my time to keep the fire alive. I bring in wet wood and pile it around the fire hoping it will dry enough to burn. I can't let the fire die out.

The rain squalls arrive in wave after wave. I never get fully dried out. I have made futile efforts to build another fire, more in the open. So far, no luck. It just sput-

*ters and blinks out. The rescue planes will never see our
fire where we have it now. I haven't heard any planes yet,
but it has been awful stormy.*

*I have never been so alone. I can't even banter with
The Monkey. I don't think he will get better.*

September 26th.

"You have done a fine job with the fire, Sis," he
said.

"Well, welcome back," I said. His voice sounded
fairly strong.

"You must be feeling better to be able to critique
my work," I said.

"I didn't mean to criticize you. You are doing OK,
really, you are doing fine," he said.

I could tell by his tone that he was not looking
for a fight today. He went on to say, "Discouraging
you is the last thing I want to do. We must keep up
our spirits and our hope. That is critical, Sis."

"Frankly, " I said, "our situation does not lend
itself to a heap of optimism."

"That's where you are wrong," he said. "We are
alive. The pilot can't say that."

"That is one way to look at it I suppose," I said.

"And another way to look at our situation," he
said, "is to know that we have experienced the worst.
It can't get any worse. So that means it has to get
better, right?"

His strange form of logic had something missing, but despite myself I did find it of some comfort.

I explained my attempt to set a signal fire more

out in the open. He supported the idea. He thought about it a bit.

"I agree with you, we should have some plans, since a plane may make only one pass over us," he said. "The problem is you will not be able to keep a big enough fire going in this rain. It won't be seen anyway."

He became silent again but I could tell he was rolling an idea around in his head.

Finally he said, "We need more of a Roman candle effect. I think I would lay a fire in the dry cover under that dead cedar tree that you stripped the bark from for the blankets. Cedar will flash fast. From the pile of dead cedar boughs at the base of the tree, the fire will shoot to the top of the tree. That could even torch nearby trees and we have a real burner for a quick signal. It wouldn't be missed. A few weeks ago I wouldn't have suggested this because we may have set off a fire that we could not control, but in this weather and at this time of year, I am not worried."

I nodded agreement. A fire out of control was not an immediate problem with buckets of water still dumping down from the heavy clouds.

"But the important thing," he said, "is that we have a plan. We always have to have a plan and a backup plan in case the first one goes sour on us."

That was the most I had heard him talk at one time. He definitely was much better.

"So," I said, "our plan for today is to lay a fire that will be ready to be touched off at the first sound of a plane or helicopter. What is the backup plan?"

"You get the signal fire ready and I will figure

out the next steps for us," he said.

I was back in less than an hour.

"What is the next plan?" I asked. I figured he would have one.

"What we are talking about here is survival," he said, "that's the basis of all our plans."

"You mean to stay alive until they rescue us," I said. It was not intended to be a question.

"No, that is not what we are about," he said. "I mean survival. We must assume that there will be no outside help. No rescue. Just us."

"That is ridiculous," I said. "Of course there will be a rescue. The search is probably in full swing right now, even in spite of the bad weather and poor visibility. No, you can be sure they are looking for us." I felt I had to convince him even more. "Hey, you don't know my dad. If people weren't out there looking there would be hell to pay. You don't know my dad. He has a lot of influence in Seattle".

"I don't think we will be found," he said. "No disrespect is intended to your father, but I don't think we will be found."

"That is a hell of a thing to say," I said.

His calmness and this matter-of-fact line of conversation made me angry.

"This is the fourth day since the crash, I believe," he said. "Have you heard any planes?"

"It will take a little time to get things organized," I said. "You know yourself that the weather has been bad.

He interrupted my arguments."How does a search work?" he asked. It was an honest question.

"I mean, wouldn't they search where they would

hope to find whatever they are looking for?" he said.

"Naturally, I suppose," I said.

"We got problems then, Sis. Because we are not anywhere near where anyone would be looking. We are not where they expect us to be."

"My God, we may be lost," I said. My obvious observation struck him as hilarious.

"You know what I mean," I said, between eruptions of our laughter.

When we had calmed down, he explained his thinking.

"Seriously," he said, "if the guy filed a flight plan, which we don't know for sure if he did, we would be a long way off it. He flew at least thirty minutes at right angles to our route. Remember, he was busy showing you the many layers of mountains? You said you were really impressed. Do you remember that? I remember how impressed he was impressing you, that he didn't pay any attention to the weather coming in."

*I don't need this.*I started to interrupt his diatribe but he had more to say.

"The pilot then spent about ten minutes trying to find a way through the clouds and another ten minutes circling before he flew us into the ground. In short, we are a long way from where reasonable people would be looking for us. If a plane flies over, it will be totally by accident; Not by any plan."

I made no response, but I noted for later reference, that he did blame me for this mess. I won't challenge that right now. *Perhaps I did contribute some, but it was not my responsibility to fly the damn plane.*

How was I supposed to know we had a renegade pilot?
  The Monkey rolled over and pretended to sleep. It was time for another wood-gathering trip and I needed a little time to think. Would it ever stop raining?

Chapter 4

If It Moves It Can Be Eaten

September 27th

S o, what is the plan?" I asked
        " I don't have a full plan yet, but first we
        eat," he said. "Then we will take an inventory of what we've got."

I was so pleased, I smiled to myself. I had outwaited him. He brought up food first. I did not share my small private victory with him. I was over the worst of the hunger pangs, but it had been a long, long time since my last meal.

"I'm all for eating, only what?" I asked.

"Getting food on a day-by-day basis won't be too hard," he said.

"Sure, I will just grab a two-for-one coupon and run right out to McDonalds," I said.

He didn't understand, and went right on as though I had made no comment.

"But getting enough food to lay ahead to see us

through the winter and for the walk out next spring, won't be that easy," he said.

"I repeat, what are we going to eat?" I asked. I was not trying to be funny now.

"In a pinch," he said, "anything that moves can be eaten, and a lot of things that don't move."

"Present company excluded, I assume," I said. He got a grin out of that.

"Well, Sis, stranger things have been recorded," he said. "I am not too worried for myself, since you have already said on several occasions how skinny I am. I would not make a full meal I suppose, but you, Sis, now that's a different story."

"You got me there," I said, "I would make several meals. But I want to go back to something you said before you started eye-balling me like a cannibal. 'What do you mean, walk out next spring'? Hey, if I am going to walk out of here, I am going to get started. None of this 'next spring' crap." I was as emphatic as I could be.

His answer came slow and deliberate. "I wouldn't blame you if you tried to walk out now," he said. "I would never try to talk you out of it or try to stop you, even if I could. But I doubt if you could make it alone."

"For criminee sake, I wouldn't leave you by yourself, all alone. I didn't mean that," I said, "I could support you as you walked."

"Then I know you wouldn't make it," he said. "You would have to go by yourself. If the tables were turned and you had the gimp legs, I might make it. But you? No, you wouldn't have a chance. For example, which way would you go? And another thing, the leaves on the vine maple have already turned colors. When will we get the first snow? You had better be to the coast, or at least at a much lower elevation, before the snow caught you. How long do you estimate it would take you, even if by some chance you went in the right direction? What would you eat?"

I had about had it with his doomsday comments.

"What do we have to eat now?" I said, "or did I miss something?"

"I think we will eat tonight but it will depend on how well you can follow instructions," he said. "We are not in a good situation but the problems are solvable. We have to do things together, as a team. My brains and experience and your legs. By the time my legs heal in four to six weeks hopefully you will be smarter."

Can you believe this kid? Apparently he never even learned to read, and he is talking about me getting smarter. I didn't waste all my time at the university. I will bite my tongue for now, but there will be a day of reckoning.

I did what he said, and by golly, we did eat, and eat well. The crawdads were where he said I would find them.

"Only small crawdads for now," he said, "the larger ones will come later."

I grabbed them behind the pinchers as he had instructed. I was fascinated with the fact that there was no way they could pinch me, no matter how hard they tried. I garnered all my nerve and broke their tails off. I wish Mom could see me now. She would never believe this. The tails were to be used as fish bait.

"Not enough to the little ones to eat," he had said.

I put the remains of the little crawdads in a pile in the slack water of the pond. I tested the woven cedar fish line that he had made. I attached the line to the end of a willow stick about five feet long. He had fashioned the hook from a pin I had.

I took careful note of my shadow, just as he had showed me. I was ready to fish—for only the second time in my life. These circumstances were much different from when I took my first fishing trip with my Dad. .

The Monkey had cautioned me, I would need to experiment. He had said, "Don't be too anxious. Let them catch themselves. Don't pull the hook out of their mouths, let them take it deep, if they will. You may only get one chance, so make the most of it."

There was too much to remember. But I was all set up and so with trepidation I swung line, hook, and bait into the water with a splat. By God, with the first attempt I had a fish. I jerked so hard that the poor fish landed the full length of my line behind me. I was on that poor devil like a cat. It was about ten inches long and the most beautiful thing I have ever seen.

Imagine, it's the first fish I have ever caught in my life. I resisted the temptation to run back to the shelter to show the fish to The Monkey. *I still have my bait. I didn't even lose my bait.*

About every other attempt produced a fish. I couldn't believe it. I knew The Monkey had hoped against hope that I might catch just one fish. I stopped when I had ten fish. They ranged in size from ten inches, which was the most frequent size, to one that was at least fifteen inches long. The fish were thick, if that's the right way to describe fish.

I have to admit, I was proud of my efforts, and when I showed the fish to The Monkey he didn't even try to hide his delight.

"Sis, I mean to tell you, you learn fast," he said.

Those words of praise were worth more than a hundred dollars to me. I sat down and he listened with intensity, as I went through each catch—the way, I suppose, deep sea fishermen would review their trophy catches.

He opened the fish with a deft slice of his knife, and removed the intestines with his thumb.

"Now for more instructions," he said. "Take the guts down by the stream but don't put them in the water. Make several small piles on the shore where you know where they are. Next, wash the fish good. Then we will need some mud from the meadow, not from the creek bank. Creek bank mud will taint the fish. Bring the mud back to me and I will mud the fish."

"You want me to wash the fish so we can put mud on them?" I said.

"That's the way we bake the fish so they won't burn to a crisp," he said. "I will show you."

I did as he had instructed. It took several trips, but he kept encouraging me. He spoke with caution, told me to walk not run and watch my step. On the last trip he reminded me of the remains of the small crawdads that he had instructed me to put in the slack water of the pond.

"Go see what you have," he said, "if you don't have some big crawdaddies, I will be surprised."

There must have been a dozen huge crawdads feeding and fightingover the remains of the smaller ones. I only managed to capture three. Crawdads can move backwards to escape, faster than I could have imagined. I removed their tails, which were as large as prawns, and threw the remains back in the same location in the slack water.

"We can eat the tails raw," he said, "but they are better lightly roasted."

"I am not ready for them raw," I said, "I'm not that hungry." He broke the mud off one of the baked fish to inspect it.

"Perfect, perfect, "he said. "If you are not too tired, you could get us some salad to go with the fish."

"Sounds fine," I said,"where do I get salad?"

"Take a long stick and drag some watercress off the top of the pond, " he said.

"Watercress? You mean like at the fancy French restaurants?" I asked.

"I sure wouldn't know anything about that, Sis, but I do know watercress when I see it, and there is watercress on the pond," he said.

It would be dark early tonight, and the rain had started once again, but it didn't seem so bad because tonight we had a feast. It was a meal I will never forget.

"Things always look better on a full stomach,"
he said. I certainly agreed with that. I found myself
jabbering away. He never had an opportunity to say
much, or at least, he chose not to. A cup of coffee
and a cigarette would have been the perfect way to
conclude the evening.

I wanted to talk more but he had curled up and
was now fast asleep. This ticked me off in a way. I
had done all the work. The least he could have done
was stay awake a little longer.

I was up early the next morning to go back to
fishing. This was exciting. The fish entrails that I had
placed in three piles on the bank, were all gone, just
as he had predicted. In the same place, however,
were many tiny tracks in the sand. The tracks all led
to the water's edge.

"Raccoons, our future meals," he said. "The
tracks to the water are evidence of the practice the
raccoons have of washing everything before they eat
it. My Gramps would give them sugar cubes. If you
ever saw something funny that was it."

"I see where you get your mean streak," I said.

We both laughed at the story. He was laughing
at the prank, and I was laughing at the way he told
the story.

Tonight we had our fill again of fish, crawdad
tails, and watercress.

"From this time on," he said, "until we leave this
place, we will think of nothing else but food, shelter, and warmth. Getting food to eat and keeping
warm will take all our time. If we don't work hard
now we will never make it through the winter ."

The weather had greatly improved today. By afternoon it was sunny and warm. A beautiful fall day. I listened through the day for planes or helicopters, but none came.

Chapter 5

Will You Talk About Me?

September 29

The Monkey's legs look much better. He has fashioned better splints and a better crutch. He still tries to keep his left leg immobilized as much as possible.

My spirits were lifted after our second big meal. By morning, I was hungry again, however.

This fishing is exciting. Today I plan to run two lines, if we can rig up another hook.

"This brings us to the next part of our plan," he said. "We need to take an inventory of what we have and what we need to make."

I looked around. "That shouldn't take long. I don't see a hell of a lot to inventory," I said.

"Our super market is the wreckage of the plane, he said. "Today the plan will be as follows; first haul more wood, then catch our supper. While I am baking the fish, you should go back to the crash site and scrounge anything that isn't burned too badly.

Anything and everything may be useful later on, anything."

I nodded, I fully understood.

He said, "I had a duffel bag full of new clothes. It was put in the storage compartment. That would be very helpful if you can find it."

I did not look forward to a return to the wreck site, but I could see the importance of doing it, and I was the only one who could.

The sun broke warm and it burned the dew off the grass and the forest floor. It was going to be a nice day, at least with respect to the weather. Perhaps the sun shining was a good omen.

Nothing had been disturbed. The pilot still lay the short distance from the plane where I had dragged him. I kicked some leaves over him, but I averted my eyes from his face.

I returned in less than two hours with my finds. He seemed a little surprised to see me back so soon. He looked over my loot with less enthusiasm than I had expected, even though I had found his duffel bag. I had not found my little carry-on bag however.

He looked over the stuff as I laid it out. There was a cushion, the duffel bag, about ten feet of wire that I was able to break loose, a sun visor, and one leather glove. He stooped and picked up the glove, the only interest he showed in any of the items.

"Oh yes," I said, "I found this spiral notebook with this ball point pen attached."

He didn't appear to hear me. He seemed to be waiting for something. After several minutes of testing the damn glove he looked up.

"Is this it?" he said. "Is this only the first trip, or

what?"

"No, that's all I could find without picking around too much," I said.

I was not prepared for his reaction. For the first time he lost his cool. I mean he was mad.

"Without picking around too much?" he sputtered, "I can't deal with this."

He began to hop around on one leg with his new crutch, muttering something under his breath. He finally began to calm down and I was glad. I had the good sense to keep my mouth shut. I knew I would soon find out what had gotten into him. This was not the time to say the wrong thing.

In a voice as calm as a minister's, he said, "Let's eat now. The fish are baked to a tee. After we have eaten we will talk about tomorrow's plan, OK?"

The meal was good but I didn't enjoy it as I should have. I was waiting for the other shoe to drop. I couldn't stand the silence any longer.

"Let's talk," I said, "it is obvious that you were expecting something from the plane that I didn't find."

He stirred up the fire with slow methodical pokes and then sat down on my cushion, which I had packed from the plane.

"Let me begin this way," he said, "the pilot wasn't naked, was he?"

"No, he wasn't naked. What kind of an off-the-wall question is that?" I said.

"Well, Sis, let me tell you , he will be before you are done, if you do your job. I want his shoes, his belt, if he has one, his billfold, his shirt, his pants, socks, even his snotrag. I want everything. I want you to use your imagination. Take the plane apart. I want every piece of glass you can find. I want it all."

"Yea, I guess I did see some glass, but I am no grave robber"—

He didn't let me finish my sentence. He raised his hand and waved for silence. He got it.

"You brought a little wire, but I want it all, rip it out," he said. He went on non-stop.

"There must be lots of electrical and steel wire on the plane. We need it, so why didn't you get it? Look for anything that will hold water. Get all the fabric or any other material you can. If you can't get it loose, take my knife and cut it loose. If you can remove any rivet or screw, bring it back. The rubber tires will burn. If you can't get them off cut them off, if you can't cut them off , then shave them with the knife. You got one sun visor, where is the other one? Get all the glass."

"You already said glass," I said. "I got it. I will get the glass."

"Get the glass," he said. "Glass can be used as a scraper, or to cut things, or as a weapon. Get any paper, wet or dry, you must use your imagination."

He had hit on an issue that I was reluctant to bring up while he was in his present state of mind. I had to credit the kid for his sharp perceptions. He had a knack for picking up on little signs.

"What is the problem?" he said.

"I know now that I can be much more imaginative and innovative than I was this afternoon, and I can see the need for any scrap of paper, but let's not use up the notebook. Would that be all right?"

I could hear the plea in my voice, and I wished it weren't there.

"Do you want it to write in?" he asked.

"Yes, I want to keep notes or something, a diary I guess," I said.

He looked at me for a long moment. I was ready to concede, and say, "Forget it."

"I think that is fine," he said.

I was shocked with his response. I thought I was going to have to sell him a little more on the idea.

"I know it is not practical thinking, but if we ever need the paper for a fire or something like that, we could tear the pages out then," I said.

"No, Sis, write the log. Will you go back and catch up on what has happened so far?"

"I could, I suppose. Do you think I should?" I said. He nodded. But I could tell that something was bothering him.

"What is it?" I asked.

"Will you talk about me in your diary?" he asked.

"How could I keep an accurate account of the events of the last week or so, not to mention the future, without writing about you?" I said.

Something was still not right with him.

"What now?" I asked.

"Will you call me Monkey in your diary?" he asked.

"Not if you have a name," I said. "I will call you whatever you wish." I was sincere and I knew he sensed that.

"My name is Donovon," he said. He said it softly again but with pride.

"My name is Donovan McDowell."

"What? Donovan? Did you say Donovan?" I said.

There was something about it that struck me as funny. I don't know what name I was expecting but Donovon wasn't it. I started to laugh. I could not help myself. He reared back his head and started to laugh too. What a relief.

"My mother's maiden name was Donovan," he said. "She married a McDowell. My Gramps called me Donny. He didn't like the name Donovan either, although that was his last name. But I can tell you he liked the name McDowell a heck of a lot less."

"I don't know if I can handle Donovan or not," I said. I started to laugh again.

He got up on his crutch and with a great flourish and a sweeping bow he said, "Monkey McDowell, at your service."

He lost his balance and would have fallen, except I caught him. We teetered for a moment and then we both sprawled to the ground. We laid there laughing, legs, splints, crutch, and arms all tied up together. I soon sensed he was uncomfortable with the situation, and he broke off. A bit shy, I thought. That's kind of cute.

"Is that Donovan with one N or two N's?" I said.

"How ever you spell Donovan," he said.

It was a welcome respite from the serious business of survival, but I thought it was curious that he didn't ask me what my name was.

Long after we had turned in for the night, he called over to me.

"At the plane tomorrow, look for a survival kit of some sort. I seem to remember that all planes that originate in Alaska have to carry a survival kit, or a box, or something like that. I think it is a state law. If there is one, it should be located in the cockpit or some place where the pilot could get to it."

The fun of the evening was over. His mind was back on business.

Chapter 6

The Box

September 30

I was back to the plane at sunrise the next morning. The forest was wet with dew and it was chilly, but it was going to be another nice day. Someone may find us today. It should be excellent flying weather. I checked the pile of brush at the base of the cedar tree as I went by. It was still dry and ready for a match to set it off if needed.

I did the most unpleasant tasks first. Some of the pilot's clothing had begun to mildew. I blanked everything out of my mind and worked as quickly as I could. It may have been chilly, but the perspiration was running down my forehead. When I had finished I placed the leaves back over him and added a layer of rocks.

The thought of a survival kit intrigued me. I squeezed my way into the cockpit. Under the jump seat in the back, in a recessed compartment I found what I was looking for. It was a pine box, a foot and a half wide by two feet long and a foot deep. It had the most beautiful words in the world stamped on it: EMERGENCY/SURVIVAL.

The box was inside a burlap gunnysack. Our luck was holding. Wedging the box against the frame of the plane was a brand new sleeping bag, still in its plastic cover. *This should be mine.*

With a great deal of maneuvering I was able to get the box out still intact. I didn't even have to unload it.

I could now see many items besides the box that we could use. My imagination was at work. It had only been resting the day before. I decided to take the things first that might deteriorate in the weather and dampness. This would include such things as the seat covers and the cloth head liner. Items such as wire and his damn glass would not be affected by the weather, so these items could wait for later trips.

I could see it would take many trips to complete the job. I can understand why The Monkey was disturbed after looking at my little load the previous day. I decided that the "survival kit" had to go out on my first trip, even though it was waterproof, since I knew it would get me out of the doghouse. I said aloud, "Wait till he sees what is in the box."

He saw me coming and guessed what was in the burlap bag. He waved to me to hurry.

No, by God. He is always the one telling me to slow down.

I took my time coming in. I loved every minute of it.

The box was a master of design except nothing

was provided to remove the staples that nailed the lid shut. If The Monkey had not had his knife, it could have been a problem. The box weighed five or six pounds. Every item had its special place and it all fit together like sardines in a can.

There was a list of contents, which is fortunate, because we would not have recognized some of the items otherwise. He had me read the list while he located each item. Most of the items had numbers on them, which corresponded with numbers on the list. This was very helpful.

Here is the list:

Box to hold 5-lb. survival kit.

Illustration of-desert still. "That's all we need, something to make more water," I said.

Fishing net—for catching bait for fishing. "This will make catching crawdads a snap," I said.

Bandanna—for neck, tie, sling, or hat. "It is too small for much of a sling, but it will be used," the Monkey said.

Cutter insect repellent. We looked a long time for this. "Cutter" seemed to be a brand name. I think The Monkey was hoping for some blade or something that would cut. I showed him the little brown bottle with the matching number. He could not imagine that they would include anything like bug repellent, which he considered frivolous, in a survival kit.

Waterproof matches. "Just like an insurance policy," he said.

Packages of synthetic kindling—to start fires. "I
am certainly glad they told us what it was
for," he said. "Did they think we might eat
it? Synthetic? does that mean that it really isn't
kindling after all?" We kept looking for more
because the list suggested that there was
more than one bundle. So who's complain-
ing. I told The Monkey we would take it up
with the Better Business Bureau at the very
first opportunity.He either didn't get it or he
didn't think it was funny.

Lens—to start fire by using sun. The Monkey said,
"It will work, but it takes a long time, and
when you need to make a fire, the sun is never
out. However, the lens has many other uses,
like for quill picking."

*Now it is my turn not to get it. He didn't ask me
to explain the Better Business Bureau, and I'11
be damned if I will ask him about picking quills.*

Candle—to assist fire lighting. "This is a good one,"
he said.

Metal match. The Monkey is thinking about this
item. I guess he will experiment with it later.

Water purifying tablets. "We won't be needing
them," he said.

Burlapbag—to hold box. "Not any more," he said.
"We have better uses for it now."

Compass. I thought a compass would be a very
important thing but The Monkey didn't think
a compass was all that critical.

Scissors and tweezers. "Good for a thousand uses,"

he said, "anything that cuts or pulls is great.
It will work fine with the lens for quill picking." He chuckled. *Some inside joke, I guess.*
Disposable razor. *I was going to make a comment
that may have been funny, but then again it may
not have been, so I kept it to myself.*
Chapstick. I was waiting for some remark, like
where is the perfume? He surprised me by
saying, "There will be times when Chapstick
will be useful."
Flares and smoke grenade. *We are not sure we understand the directions and we certainly can't experiment. We both feel more comfortable with our
preparations to torch the cedar tree in case we ever
do hear an airplane.*
Disposal scalpel blades. "If it cuts it is good," he
said.
Disposable soap, tube. "We will save this for a time
when one of us has a cut or an open wound,
he said. That is not such a happy thought.
Sharpening stone. He was very glad to have the
stone.
Floating knife. The Monkey said he would make
a belt scabbard for me, and the knife would
be mine. *He thinks his own knife is a better one
or he would have taken the new one himself.*
**Folding knife—smeared with Vaseline and wrapped
in plastic.** We decided to leave this knife
wrapped as it is, and keep it for a spare.
Disposable flashlights. Again, the list suggested
more than one, but there was only one that
we could find. "It works and it is pretty
good," he said, "and look, if you turn the lens

it can be a spot light or a floodlight. We will
be stingy with it."

Aluminum foil—for signaling or cooking. "In our
case it won't be for signaling," The Monkey
said.

Folding saw. The Monkey called it a "bow saw."
Apparently it has a good blade. "It will work
fine for us if we don't horse it too much," he
said.

Fishing gear. "Does this mean we can retire my
cedar line?" I asked. "We will wait to see if
you can catch any fish with it first," he said.

Nylon line.

Wire snares. He had never seen snares made of
wire I guess. I have never seen snares period,
made of wire or anything else. He had
planned to use something else to snare small
game, but he was excited about the wire ones.
He worked the loops and studied them for
quite awhile.

**Emergency space blanket—sitting on a larger space
blanket.** "I wish they were both much larger,"
I said.

Whistle. I made the mistake of playing down the
whistle and got a free lecture on the value of
the whistle. "This one is yours," he said. "I
will make one for me from a piece of copper
tubing from the plane. We will wear them
around our necks at all times. With a whistle
you can communicate across creeks or can-
yons where the human voice won't carry as
well. If you have to make repeated signals,
like if you're lost, the whistle saves energy. A
whistle has a much greater range than your

voice and the sound of a whistle can be picked out over other sounds in nature. Also a whistle can pipe you home like a ship in the fog if you can't see for any reason."

The last comment woke me up a little. "Under what circumstances would a person lose their vision and not be able to see?" I asked. "There could be a number of situations," he said, "all of them bad. For example, snow blindness, or snow just too heavy to see through, night time of course, a blow on the head, eyes swollen shut for any reason, such as from poison oak or stinging nettles, or extreme malnutrition..."

"O.K.,O.K. I get the picture," I said, "and two little whistles will help all of that?"

"You bet. We will experiment with the range and we will eventually get to where we can almost talk to each other just by using the whistles," he said. "We can say stop or go, come here, help, hurry, slow, yes or no, S.O.S. count numbers, and on and on. The whistle improves hand signals because the sound of the whistle can first get your attention so that you can then look for the hand signals. The whistle can be used in everyday situations. It doesn't have to be only dramatic situations. But we have to practice. In some situations that I can think of a person would not come all the way into camp without first giving a signal and then waiting for a return response."

"You make it sound like a telephone," I

said.

"Yes, I guess so," he said. "Let's get back to work."

Stainless steel mirror—for signaling. "That is more like if you were in a boat on the water," he said.

Can opener. "Great! now if we just had some cans to open, I bet it would work fine," I said.

Salt. The salt was in tablet form. The Monkey said, "Too bad there isn't about fifty pounds of salt. We could use it for curing meat."

Sewing kit. There were three needles of different sizes and a nice assortment of threads. "How are you at sewing?" he asked.

I wrinkled up my nose, and he laughed.

Nylon cord. It was in a coil with a metal clip on it to keep it from tangling. We didn't uncoil it but it looked like about twenty feet of cord. I commented on the fact that the cord was so small in diameter that it would cut into a person's hands if one pulled something heavy. "That's why they call it a cord and not a rope," he said.

Distress panel orange marker. This was similar to a long pennant flag. When it was unfolded it was about five feet long.

Folding camp shovel. The Monkey was intrigued with the clever way the handle telescoped down to only the length of the shovel blade. This made the overall length only about ten inches. He didn't think much of the handle.

"It won't take much strain," he said. He
planned to replace the handle with a stronger one made of wood.
Steel-handled hatchet. "This is very, very important. I am glad the handle is made of steel,"
he said. I was sure that comment was made
for my benefit. The axe or hatchet was the
last item in the box, but on the bottom of the
list was a notation which said: ".22 cal.rifle.
(broken down)clipped to side of
box-optional." The clips were there but there
was no rifle. You could plainly see where
there had been a stock and a detachable bar-
rel with another clip that held a box of shells.
But it was not there now. "Are you sure it
wasn't some place else in the plane?" he
asked. I thought he was going to cry. "If it
had been stored inside the box it would still
be there," he said. "On the outside it would
have been too easy to get to, for plunking tin
cans or who knows what."

We laid our treasures out and inspected each one
several times before we turned in for the night. We
could not even come close to restoring all the gear
back into the box.

"Tomorrow night we will eat something besides
fish and crawdads ," he said. "We will eat rabbit or
raccoon or whatever we can snare."

That sounded good to me. I was ready for something hardier than fish. Even raccoon didn't sound
too strange.

"We would have had a chance to make it with

the gun wouldn't we?" I said.

"We will make it anyway. The gun would just have made it easier, a lot easier," he said.

Chapter 7

The Reward

October 6th

I t had frosted for several nights, hard enough for ice to form on the edges of the pond.
"It is only the second week of October, and it is cold enough to freeze ice," I said. "Winter must be coming early."

He shook his head. "I don't think winter is early but it is coming," he said. "The vine maples had already turned colors before we got here, and the alder leaves are dropping now. I put our elevation at about seven thousand to eight thousand feet. I judge those peaks to be about ten thousand feet because timberline would be nine thousand or so and the peaks poke up beyond the timberline."

"So, what are you saying?" I asked.

"I'm saying that at this elevation it isn't early fall, but late fall. The next moisture that falls will dust those peaks with snow, which is to say, we do not have much time left to prepare for winter."

He had more to say, and he had my attention. "This brings up a major concern for us." He said. "We can't stay here in this little shelter much longer. It is too exposed. We need better protection from the weather and we need more room."

His points were well taken. Most of the gear and materials that I brought from the plane have had to stay outside our dugout shelter. Although it has not rained for a week, it was just a matter of time before the weather would turn bad again and drench every item not under cover.

"What do you have in mind?" I asked.

"I have been studying that rock pile down the canyon," he said. He pointed to a pile of rubble about three-fourths of a mile downstream and at a lower elevation.

"It could be," he said, "that on that bench above the creek we could roll enough rocks together to form a wall, and we could lean poles against it to make a bigger and more protected cover. I don't know what you will find once you get down there, but I don't want us to locate too far from the creek and the pond. The creek is still our best source of food."

"So, you think that I should become a scout," I said.

"Get some sleep. Tomorrow will be a big day for you," he said. "I will have a few suggestions for you before you leave in the morning."

A few suggestions? More like orders. He can't think of anything right now, so he will stay awake coming up with something..

One thing about sleeping with nature, we didn't need an alarm clock. At about a half-hour before sun-up the canyon came alive. If it wasn't the blue jays scolding away, it was the kingfisher squawking like an army bugler.

The Monkey was up to break the dry mud off a trout we had left cooking in the coals over night. It was time to go exploring. Now for his orders.

"Don't cross the creek." he said. "Don't go any higher up the canyon wall than you have too. If you do go up, never let the creek get out of your sight, OK? "

"Are you afraid I will get lost?" I said.

"Stranger things have happened," he said. "Take this bag with you, tie it around your waist, so you will have your hands free."

"What's in the bag?" I asked.

"Some dry moss, two of the waterproof matches, your knife, because I have not been able to make a scabbard for it yet, and a trout wrapped in foil. It is all light-weight. You have your whistle on, I hope"

I had an urge to make some smart remark but I thought better of it. He had done some serious planning and I decided I should not downplay it.

"Finally," he said, "don't hurry, pick your way."

I was eager to get started. I had not had the time or the excuse to explore downstream. With a wave, I was gone.

*   *   *   *   *   *   *   *   *   *   *   *   *   *   *   *   *

The moon had been up for an hour by the time I walked into camp. I had not lost track of the time. I had had things to do. I could smell the aroma of the meat cooking before I got to the shelter. He was up on his feet and waiting at the outer ring of light from the fire. It was a huge fire he had going. He thought I needed a beacon. He had obviously been moving around quite a bit more than any time since the crash. I could see the results in the size of the wood pile and the fresh meat, which he must have snared.

"I said pick your way, pick your way, not crawl like a snail," he greeted me. "Where have you been for so many hours?"

"I took the wrong freeway and before you knew it I was clear through to San Francisco and—." It cracked him up.

"OK, OK, let's eat," he said, "then we can talk."

He handed me a charred stick with something speared on it. I didn't ask him what it was. Although the morsel was burned to a crisp it tasted good. He could tell I had lots to share, but I ate slowly, chewing every chunk until it was like rope.

"I have found our new Hilton Hotel," I said. "The pile of rock is from a slide from further up the mountain."

"Is it a fresh slide?" he asked.

I could see there would be many interruptions, but I was ready for them.

"No, it's not a fresh slide at all," I said. I was ready for that question. I had several comments ready to make to support my conclusion, but he didn't ask for any additional data.

I continued, "The river at some time, undercut the rock cliff like a knife cutting a wedge out of a cake. It has left an overhang that runs for over two hundred feet, I stepped it off. The cut goes back into the cliff twenty feet. The roof tapers down, but I can walk in at least fifteen feet in most places before I have to stoop over."

"Is it dry?" he asked.

"It is bone dry."

"There is a huge logjam on the creek just below the out cropping of rock," I said, "so our wood supply will be easier to get. From the floor of the cut, or cave, as I would describe it, you can see up and down the valley for a much greater distance than we can from here. I could see the smoke from your fire and I could tell when you added more wood." I stopped to catch my breath I could tell he was trying to picture all that I was describing. He was hanging on every detail and I had lots more to say.

"If we build the fire in front of the cut," I said, "we will capture much more heat than we can here. The heat won't just go out into empty space, which means we will not need as big a fire, which means less time needed to gather wood, and..."

He raised his hand. "Slow down, slow down a bit, " he said.

"I guess I was talking pretty fast," I said. "You may have to blow that whistle of yours, only I can't remember how many blasts mean stop."

I was hoping he would not come up with some perfectly logical problem that I had missed in my scouting report to deflate my bubble.

"Well, it certainly sounds like it would be an improvement over our current setup," he said. "However, I am not sure we can capture much more heat in a two-hundred-by-twenty foot slice in the rock."

I was not going to be discouraged . "We can cut

off the area with a pile of rocks to form a wall, or
two walls, if we want. That's why I call it a cave," I
said. "We can pile the rocks all the way to the ceiling
of the cut and stuff moss or mud into the cracks to
make it weather-tight. We have lots of building material available to do the job."

"It will take a lot of rocks if I have the situation
pictured straight," he said.

"You bet it will," I said. I could hardly contain
my enthusiasm. "And I have one wall over half done.
What do you think I have been doing for the last
nine hours?" I gestured with my hand to the height
that the wall had been constructed. He reached out
and grabbed my waving hand, then he grabbed my
other hand at the wrist and turned them both palms
up. My hands were cut and scraped and generally a
mess, but they did not hurt as bad as they looked.
Once again I was surprised at his strength, as I resisted his turning my hands over. He held both of
my hands and looked me straight in the eyes until I
felt awkward. I was glad when he dropped my
hands, but he kept looking at me.

"My hands don't hurt much," I said. I figured a
little fib wouldn't hurt anything.

"That's good," he said, "because it sounds like
you have lots more rocks to pile."

He turned from the fire and hobbled off into the
darkness.

"Hey, I'm not through," I said. "You can do that
later." He did not answer from his veil of darkness.
He was gone long enough for my assumption to
have been correct, only, it wasn't correct. Finally he
reappeared. In his outstretched hand was a cigarette,

an honest to goodness cigarette. I couldn't believe my eyes.

"Why you little bastard, I said, "you didn't throw my cigarettes away after all."

"Let's just say that I didn't throw them all away," he said.

"As much as I hate to contribute to your bad habit," he said, "if ever a person deserved the reward of their choice, I guess it would be you tonight. Enjoy your smoke. I am going to turn in. We have much to do tomorrow."

After the first long pull on the cigarette, I said only loud enough to be sure he would hear, "That little bastard. I ought to wring his skinny neck." I could hear him chuckling as he rolled up in his tangle of cedar mats.

The cigarette did not taste as good as I had hoped. The first drag even made me a little dizzy. I was exhausted but a feeling of contentment swept over me. I had made the team.

Finally as I went to bed I thought, how nice it was of The Monkey, that he had saved back one cigarette to reward me at just the right time Then it hit me. He didn't hold back a cigarette to reward me at all. In those first few hours after the crash, a reward for me was not even remotely in his mind. He held back the cigarette in case he should need some trading stock, a bribe.

Sure he did. I will hit him up with that some day. I wonder what he thought one stale cigarette was going to get him..

Chapter 8

Happy Birthday To Me

October 20

I t took most of my time during the next week to make the move from our original shelter to the cave. The Monkey hobbled and slid to the new site.

He showed me how to make a travois like the Indians used, which enabled me to drag much larger loads: He had me cut two saplings each ten feet long. We bound them together with the nylon cord from the survival kit. This made a convenient stretcher, a platform on which to tie stuff and pile things, that would otherwise be too awkward for one person to carry.

He had good ideas, but he also had a way of making me look foolish for not thinking of the better procedure on my own. The travois was a classic example of this. After I had deposited my first load from the travois, I rolled up the cord on the two poles and started back up the creek to get another load. The Monkey was sitting on a rock watching my efforts. He started to laugh and then pretended he was about to fall off his rock from laughter. I knew his put-down laugh by this time so I knew I was in for it.

"What is your problem?" I asked.

"Do you have your initials carved in the poles?" he asked.

"Yea, sure, I have the time to carve my initials," I replied.

"Well I thought the poles had to be something very special to you. Otherwise, why would you carry the poles all the way back?" he said.

"What is your point?" I said. "I don't have the time to play games."

"You could leave those poles here and cut new ones at the other end, unless of course the poles are special to you. You see, that way, you wouldn't have to carry..."

"OK, I get it. I get it," I said. I threw the poles to the ground, and as bad luck would have it, one of the poles pivoted over a boulder and cracked me hard on the shin. I resisted the impulse to rub my shin and turned quickly so that he did not see me blinking back tears.

There was no reason for him to act that way. He could have explained his point in a helpful way. But he had to come up with a put-down. Afterwards, I could always think of a good reply that would have put him in his place, but I always missed the best opportunity. For example later, I wished I had shot right back, " I don't understand, why don't you spell it out for me?"knowing full well the ignorant little hillbilly couldn't even spell his own name. *The truth, however, is that he isn't ignorant. He is smart. He is so logical. But he can't be any smarter than I am. I refuse to think that.* But he knew so many shortcuts and could apply principles in so many situations, you would have thought he was eighty years old instead of whatever. The thought of him as a little old man dressed up like a boy struck me as funny. That would explain his "wisdom" and maybe also explain his apparent lack of interest in me personally. At least my shin had stopped hurting. *He isn't smarter than I am. He is just trained to think in a different way.*

October 23.

The late October weather has turned warm and pleasant although the nights were cold. "Indian Summer,"he called it. We worked by the firelight each evening to construct the rock walls to enclose the cave. We closed off the front with a wall about my shoulder height. To enter the doorway was a bit tricky. In front of the open doorway and about three feet out he built a short wall the same width as the door. "A little baffle," he said. You had to turn partially sideways to get in and you could not come straight in the front, as it made a narrow passageway on each side. I felt that this handicapped us in bringing anything into the cave. He conceded that point, but he also felt it was best to restrict anything else from coming in.

"It's a better lash-up, " he said.

I'm not sure, and he didn't say, what it is he wants to keep out.

While I was away one day The Monkey built a short stone wall separating my sleeping area from the rest of the cave. It was aligned in such a way as to not block any heat from the fire, but it provided me with a degree of privacy. I had become accustomed to sleeping in our common area, so I had forgotten how nice it was to have a place of my very own. I admitted it was thoughtful of him.

The cave was becoming quite comfortable. We built a permanent fire pit, where the heat reflected and radiated back into the cave. The fire required only a fraction of the fuel that we had been burning before.

The nice weather tempted me to think again about walking out yet this fall. The Monkey's legs were much better but I knew he would still be slowed down. He still had a great fear of getting caught part way out in a snow storm.

It has been forty days since the crash. We have not heard a single airplane. We don't talk much about rescue. In fact The Monkey never did see an outside rescue as a possibility. We have not even taken the time to set up another signal tree to torch here near the cave. We should do that, I suppose just in case we do hear an airplane.

If I am right on my days, tomorrow is October 31,1986, a Friday, and my twenty-third birthday. I don't know if I will mention it to The Monkey or not. It will be a hard day for Mom, I know.

Chapter 9

Control Is Not As Important

November 10

The problem is not that we won't be able to get enough food to eat on a day-by-day basis," he said. "The problem is to get enough food stored ahead, to carry us against the time when we will not be able to get out."

"Do you think it will snow that much?" I said.

"We have to plan that it will, " he said. "The major problem is preserving the food."

To help solve that problem he constructed a clever stone smokehouse. It became my job to bring in green alder wood for his smoldering enclosure which was soon to be kept burning night and day.

"The fish will smoke up nicely," he said. "By that I mean, dry and hard." He ran three fish lines now. Some of every catch was smoked, even if we went to bed hungry.

The Monkey was able to get around enough to

run what we called our "short snare line," while I ran the "long snare line." My route was over rougher terrain that he could not negotiate. The level of difficulty of the two routes was not the only difference, however. The main difference was that he was successful and I was not. He snared something almost every day and I snared nothing.

This was a serious matter. He felt that we had to get some production out of both lines. He was very patient, and showed me the principles of the snare many times, but there was something I was not doing right. Finally, he watched me one day and came up with the conclusion that I was not careful enough with what he called, "leaving scent."

"I bend over at the waist to set the snare," he said, "You kneel on both knees. This leaves too much scent."

I tried to do it his way but it was too difficult. So, he coached me on how to crush ferns and rub them on my hands and on the knees of my pants.

"If it is easier for you, kneel to make the set," he explained, "all we have to do is kill the scent trace you leave behind."

There were other tips as well. For example: I stepped on branches, but he stepped over them. He ducked and squeezed under limbs, where I brushed through them. He even used the tactic of following a rabbit-run up-hill to the place he planned to set his snare. This meant extra steps. I asked him, "Why do you come back up-hill?"

"Maybe you haven't noticed, but the breeze comes down the mountain slopes each evening," he said. "That is because the air cools down at night higher up the mountain. The cold air is heavier, and so it flows downhill, carrying any scent I may be leaving behind, away from my snare. Most of the critters are snared at night. If they were daytime animals, you would do it just the opposite."

"How do you know all that stuff?" I asked. He just shrugged.

In any case, something started to work for me, because suddenly I was getting a rabbit or raccoon nearly every day. One day I even snared a fox. I hated to kill it but I knew the Monkey would want to skin him for the fur. I did not imagine he would be interested in the meat of the fox, but I can tell you, he did not throw it away.

"He said, "It is as good as dog meat."

I wouldn't know.

"Now we will make you a real trapper," he said, "You must learn to trap and snare mountain grouse. It is not hard but the technique is altogether different. If you learn this , you will be able to trap quail, pheasant, duck, or any other bird."

Somehow I caught on to grouse trapping quickly and the change in diet was welcomed. The breast of the birds smoked up very good.

The real work began after the game was caught. In the case of fish it was comparatively simple, but in the case of any game that had fur or feathers it was more difficult. In the case of a rabbit or raccoon the animal would have to be carefully skinned and then the meat was sliced into thin strips for the smoking process.

All of this consumed time; but slowly our larder

began to fill. The "cured" meat was hard, black, and smelled like alder smoke. I accused him of storing charcoal alder chips to feed me later.

"All I can say is, " he said, "hunger is the best cook."

He kept the smoker going constantly. The wire racks he had made raised and lowered, and the strips of meat turned on the hour. Stoking the fire was a never ending chore. He did most of the preparation at night but he needed the daylight to properly observe the drying process. I never got the feel for skinning the game or stripping the meat.

"That's all right with me." he said. "There is plenty of work you can do that is too difficult for me because of my legs."

An example of this division of labor was the acorn harvest. He pointed out the tops of a grove of oak trees that grew in a side canyon. The tops were all that he could see from the cave, yet he could identify the trees as being oak. The trees were huge, but the acorns that covered the ground were small. Even so, a morning of hard picking would net me half a gunnysack of acorns.

Like the other food, the harvesting of the acorns themselves was only the start toward making the acorns edible. Acorns looked so good freshly harvested, but they were the most bitter thing I had ever tasted.

"By the time we get done with those acorns, they will be delicious," he said. He made a "water hole," which was a rock-walled vat with clay caked thick on the outside. It was not leak-proof but the water stayed in the vat for several days. He built the vat near the smoker because he used hot rocks from the fire to bring the water in the vat to a boil. Boiling water was more difficult because of our altitude. I didn't know that made a difference, but it does. He made special tongs of wood to handle the hot rocks. He boiled the acorns until the shells cracked. We then shelled the acorns and boiled them again in clean water. At least the water started clean; however, he added several handfuls of alder ash from the fire. The ash removed any remaining bitterness. The final step in the process was to spread the acorns under the hot coals of the campfire each evening. By morning the acorns would be roasted. He raked the acorns out of the ash, blew them off, and they were ready for storing. The finished product was tasty.

Nothing went to waste in The Monkey's operation. The hulls of acorns were put in another water hole filled with cold water. The pelts from any animal he had skinned were placed in the brown acorn-hull soup for a week.

"The bitterness that leaches out of the acorns is tannin," he said, "the shells of the acorns are loaded with tannin."

"I did not know where the term tanning hides came from until now," I said.

"Rhubarb root is even better," he said, "but I have not been able to look for any wild rhubarb."

After the hides had a week of soaking in the tannin The Monkey would wring all the water out of the hides and lay them over boulders to dry. He tied as many rocks to the edges of the hides that he could. This reduced shrinkage. The work area did not smell like a perfume factory but the end product was a soft pliable piece of fur and skin.

"We will use it all in some way before we are done here," he said.

I have developed more and more respect for The Monkey. It is strange but I do not have the problem of accepting his leadership anymore. I can take his direction and control with very little hesitation. In my world I would never have surrendered authority to a man, let alone a skinny boy.

This is his world, his street corner and here he is the superior. Power and control are not as important to me anymore.

Chapter 10

Marching Orders

November 20

*E*ach night he goes over the plan for the next day. "Marching orders," he calls them. He is never without a plan. We always run out of hours before we run out of plans. Sometimes we will pick up the leftovers from the plan of the day before, but just as often it will be a new plan.

I grouse about his damn plans, but to have a plan each day actually makes the time fly by. It gives me something to anticipate. This is an excellent technique to keep morale high. I don't suppose he does it for that reason, but it results in my looking forward to each day knowing that I have an important task to do. I have a purpose. I am needed. There is too much for one person to do even if he had full use of his legs. It is a good feeling to be needed.

Often the plans for the next day were in vague

terms. At first I thought he did this because he had not worked out the details . That was not the case. I learned to wait until the next morning to get the details. The specifics were often so long and exact that he thought I would forget them by the next day and he would just have to explain it all over again.

Many times I felt I just wanted to do the task and get it over with, rather than endure his step-by-step instructions.

I knew he was aware of his overly long instructions. One time he was trying to tell me where to find hazelnuts when he said, "I think you will be there before I get done telling you about it." It broke me up.

His nighttime comments were often so vague, "Can I get you to hang the flag tomorrow?"

"Hang the flag? You bet," I said. Now what in the hell did "hang the flag" mean? I didn't ask, but I was ready for anything the following morning.

"Hanging the flag" started out with me having to climb an alder tree with the bow saw tied to a cord attached to my waist. This was a carefully selected alder tree.

"What I want you to do, Sis, is to climb up this tree," he said. "Cut off the limbs as you go up."

"Wait a minute. How do I get back down?" I asked.

"I was just going to explain," he said. "You leave short limbs about ten inches long on alternating sides of the tree. What will that give you?"

"A ladder?"

"Go up as far as you feel comfortable, say about

half-way; then top the tree and come get me for the flag ceremony," he said.

The tree was easy to climb and it was fun. I had always wanted to climb trees as a girl but some one would always yell at me to come down. No one was yelling today so I enjoyed this. He said top it about half-way up, but I decided to go a little higher. I could see all over, including The Monkey working at the cave. I could see him easily, but he would have to know exactly where to look to pick me out from all the surrounding foliage. It was an intriguing sense of control for me.

When I topped the tree I had only about three inches of tree to cut through. I was at least sixty five-feet in the air. That is a long way from the ground. I had just swung to the ground when The Monkey arrived to see what was taking me so long. He looked at the pile of limbs on the ground and then started his eye slowly up the tree. He had to stand back a step to see the top.

"Did you do all that?" he asked.

"No, a very tall beaver did it," I said.

"That's good. I am glad it was the beavers because that is too high for one of us to go," he said. He handed me the orange panel marker from the survival kit and motioned me to tuck one end under my belt.

"Ensign, please raise the colors," he said.

"Aye, aye, Captain," I said. This was fun. I went swinging right up my ladder at a fast clip when he yelled to me.

"Better slow down a bit Ensign, if you get your britches snagged up there you are on your own. I'm afraid of high places," he said.

I tied the marker at about a foot from the top of the tree. It hung down five feet. The tree had been carefully selected so that it would be visible for a long distance, and with the flag of such an intense orange, it really stood out.

"So you haven't given up the hope of our being spotted," I said.

"I'm not counting on it," he said, "but since we have the pennant, we might as well put it to good use. It will also serve as an excellent weather vane."

It soon became standard practice for us to glance at the flag to determine wind direction and wind strength.

Every organization has its routine, and our organization did too. He usually figured about three hours of work to be done by firelight. We always went to bed dead tired. I got up when the cave was lighted by the morning sun. As the days were getting shorter I was getting more sack time.

The Monkey started to stir around each morning while it was still dark. His first self-assigned task was always to rake the coals together from the evening fire and rekindle the fire for a new day. My first task was to back up to the new fire and get warm.

We ate leftovers for breakfast, if there ever were any. We seldom ate lunch or "dinner" as he called it. We had our main meal for the day after dark. He called this "supper" instead of dinner.

I experienced fatigue like I never knew was possible. In the past if I got a little tired I rested, but here if I get a little tired I keep working. *In spite of fatigue I feel good. My legs are as hard as the rock walls around us. My muscles are often sore but it is a "good" soreness.* I commented to him, "Being wet as much as we have been, and always hot on one side and cold on the other, you would think we would have one long continuous head cold."

His answer made sense. "You catch colds from people. I haven't noticed too many people around," he said.

The Monkey was always making something for the cave. Whenever I came in at night from my work plan, I was often surprised to find something new added, something he had made or improvised.

"Our goal every day should be to make the cave warmer, safer, more comfortable, cleaner, or more convenient," he said.

I was surprised at how high a priority he placed on comfort.

He made one-legged stools early on. Once you got used to them they were comfortable. He made two log chairs that are truly classic in design. The legs and backs are notched into the seats. His master-pieces, however, were carved spoon-and-fork sets for each of us. The forks have two tines. He also made a big spoon and a barbed spear to stir or spike the food. The spear was particularly useful to me, because, I lost more than one morsel of meat into the fire.

He had a big thing about keeping the cave clean. We scooped and swept the sediment of a hundred years out of the cave. He even had us mop the bare rock floor with wet fir boughs.

"If we don't mop, the dust will become unbearable," he said.

He was a paradox, however, when it came to cleanliness.

I don't believe he has taken a bath since we have been here. However, he washes his hands with great care between every operation having to do with the preparation of food. He also washes his hands, forearms, and face before every meal. To wash clothing must be some kind of a sin.

I am ashamed to say, that I have taken only three baths myself, and two of those were in the first week after the crash. It is just too much trouble and too damn cold.

Here I am, a shower-a-day person, often more, with a super-sensitive olfactory mechanism and I have become totally oblivious to smells!

Chapter 11

Squirrels

November 20

As we turned the acorns in the coals one evening I asked him about squirrels.

"Are squirrels good to eat?" I asked.

"Sure they are. Somebody compared them to chicken or rabbit, only there is less to them," he said. "Why do you ask?"

"Every day when I gather acorns there are as many as six squirrels that scold the daylights out of me," I said. "They are so funny and bold. I hope it doesn't become necessary to snare any of them for food. It would be too much like eating a friend. It wouldn't be like the rabbits or other animals we trap. I don't know them as individuals. These squirrels have individual identities. I know them."

He stopped raking the acorns. "That's it. That's the answer," he said. "I should have thought of it sooner."

"Thought of what sooner?" I queried.

"I have wondered why you have not found any hazelnuts. I think your friends are the answer," he said.

The Monkey had pointed out which brush-like trees were hazelnut trees. He had drawn the distinctive leaf shape for me several times and told me how to distinguish them from other trees and brush by their fall colors.

I had looked for hazelnuts each time I went to gather acorns, but all I ever found was maybe a handful I picked up off the ground. The Monkey showed me, to my dismay, that each nut had a tiny hole in the shell where a worm had exited, leaving behind coffee grounds as remains rather than the sweet nut.

"Your squirrel friends have beaten us to the harvest," he said. He seemed pleased with the thought.

"They have left the wormy ones for us. They would never store the wormy ones," he said. "They can tell which ones are wormy some way even before the worm hatches out."

"My Gramps had a favorite story about how he made it through one tough spell on nuts that he robbed from a squirrel's hoard," he continued. "We could do the same thing. I have heard the story often enough."

"It sounds subversive to me," I said.

"No, the hoards should all be above ground," he said.

I must remember to use only one-syllable words in

the future.

"This will be the plan," The Monkey said. He gave me an hour's lecture on the lives and habits of the squirrel. "Their nests or hoards will not be in the oak grove or among hazelnut trees," he said. "Go back into the big timber. Look for piles of discarded scales from fir cones and piles of nut shells. The piles will be located at the base of a large fir or spruce tree. The piles are a dead give-away. You will find the hoard about fifteen to twenty feet up in the tree. Look for a crotch or a hole in the tree. The hole will look small but it will open up to be much larger inside.

The nuts will be stored up to a level just below where the blue jays can reach them. Does this make sense to you?" He barely slowed down to ask.

"You mean our blue jays?" I asked. He was animated as he continued his saga of a day in the life of a squirrel.

"When you find a squirrel hole, shove a stick in it," he said.

"Put a stick in the hole?" I asked.

"That's right. Then sit back and watch the squirrels. They will chatter and scold you like nothing you have heard before, but you just sit back and watch for a while, OK?"

"Sure, sit back and watch," I said.

"They will leave one squirrel to scold you but the others will scamper off to check their other hoards," he said.

This part of the story he found to be really funny. He stopped for a roaring laugh. I would bet anything that his Gramps stopped to laugh at this point in his storytelling too.

"Each squirrel will check each hoard within your radius. You get it? If you are not sure you have spotted the next hole just wait—and every squirrel will soon confirm it for you," he said.

He was prancing around, acting like the squirrels would. It was a good show, but he had still more information.

"Another indication that you are very near a hoard is when these little bickering housewives grow suddenly very quiet," he said.

I let the "housewife" remark go by. There was a time when I would've challenged a comment like that.

"When they are sure you have found their hiding place, expect to be cussed out like you have never been cussed before," he said.

"That will be something then. I do hope I am up to that part of the assignment," I said.

"Don't stick more holes than you have time to harvest, because by the time you get back they will have moved every nut in the place, and all you'll have left is a hole in a tree."

His excitement over this animal scam got me caught up in it too. I was eager to give it a try the next morning. However, there was something about it that bothered me. The Monkey sensed some reluctance on my part.

"Don't worry, Sis, the squirrels are not going to starve this winter because of the nuts we steal," he said, "if that's what is bothering you."

"That is exactly what I was wondering," I said.

"The squirrels store enough food for three win-

ters at least," he said. "In fact: some of the nuts we
find may be last year's nuts. The nuts will store forever if they stay dry. That's what is so keen about
hazelnuts."

With that information, I did feel better about the
operation

It was as if he had written the script. I found five
hoards, which even surprised The Monkey. I managed to pretty well clean them out. In several cases I
could not reach all the nuts.

The burlap bag was about one-fourth full when
I returned to the cave. The Monkey was beside himself with joy.

"Did they quiet right down when you got on top
of their hiding places?" he asked.

"Just like they had a cue from a director," I said.

"I wish I could have been there to watch," he
said.

"Watch who? The squirrels or me," I said.

He said that I should pull a raid every third or
fourth day from now until the snow gets too deep
or until they hide them better.

"It will get harder and harder as they get you
figured out," he said, "like how high up a tree you
are willing to go."

"They will get a surprise there," I said," I am
experienced at that."

We enjoyed cracking and eating hazelnuts after
dinner. No candy could have tasted better.

"We will not be ungrateful to your friends," he
said. "We will not set snares intended for them, and
if we trap one by accident we will turn it loose. OK?"

That pleased me very much and I told him as

much. He was showing some humane behavior.

"They are worth more to us alive than dead," he said. "Alive, they will continue to give us many pounds of top-quality food. Dead, they will only produce a few ounces of poor meat."

Well, so much for his kindheartedness.

Chapter 12

Special Friends

November 22

Besides the squirrels, we have gotten acquainted with many other friends of the wild. Our alarm clock each morning is a pair of blue jays. A half hour before sunrise they are up squawking, and they expect everyone in the valley to be up doing something.

"The jays are very territorial," The Monkey said.

Further down the valley there are other jays, but they should not even think about coming around the cave. That area is already claimed by "our" jays. We feed our jays underdeveloped acorns that are too small for us to mess with.

"The jays take it upon themselves to be the sentinels of the forest," he said.

I believed it. As we went from one jay territory to another the alarm was sounded up and down the line. If something that represented danger or the unknown such as a hawk or a fox entered jay space the world soon knew it.

"All the residents of the valley take heed of the jays 'early warning system'," he said, "and it will pay us, too, not to ignore it."

We watched in fascination and amusement as a fox in an attempt to stalk mice sat down in utter disgust and frustration because of the jays' warnings. The poor fox finally left the area still hungry. The jays had done it to him again.

The blue belted kingfisher was a regular also. More than once while fishing, I had the liver scared out of me by the sudden rush of the kingfisher's wings and his hysterical call.

"A hysterical scream, is the only way to describe the kingfisher's call," The Monkey said.

The kingfisher's strength however, was his patience, whether it was waiting to dash into the water to catch a four-inch trout, or the waiting for us to finish cleaning our fish. While we cleaned the fish we never saw the kingfisher, but we knew he was watching patiently, because just as soon as we would leave, he would swoop down from somewhere to start his gleaning.

Then there were the dippers. They were little short-winged birds that walked under the water behind the slide and the falls to pick at small aquatic animals, I guess. They were fascinating to watch.

We often heard more than one owl hooting to each other.

"They never hoot at the same time," he said, "which shows better manners than most people have. First, one will sound off with several hoots, and then in a few minutes it is answered by another owl."

"When the moon is full I have seen them sweep across the light, and if you were not looking, you would never know they were there, because there is no noise to their flight; total silence," he said.

A family of deer visited the creek each morning and most evenings, to drink. They were beautiful and graceful. They would arrive about an hour after sun-up, drink, graze a little, drink again, then be gone. They always came down the same little rill to get their drink. The Monkey was interested in their habits and spent time observing them from a distance.

"The deer may be our life saver," he said, "our insurance policy. I hope they continue coming when the snow is deep. That oak tree is our answer to the problem of how we get our prize."

He was referring to a large oak tree that stood near the bank where the deer drank. The oak had spreading branches as large as a man's body.

"Note," he said, "the buck raises his head to sniff the wind constantly, but he never looks up."

"It looks to me like he is always looking up," I said.

"Not really," he said, "not up into the oak tree."

I didn't like what I knew he was thinking because I did not want the deer family hurt. He didn't have a total solution to the problem, but he had started to set the stage. He went down to the tree and pulled himself up to the lowest major limb and slid back and forth on the seat of his pants. That was all he did.

We could tell the first time the deer returned that

they did smell him, because they were more nervous than usual. But after the fourth time of doing this, however, the deer paid little attention to the strange smell. They did not see it as any more of a threat than other strange smells, maybe even less. Of course that is exactly what The Monkey was counting on.

On several different nights we heard a cougar scream. This blood-chilling sound in the night was good news as far as The Monkey was concerned.

"Where there are cougar there are deer," he said.

"It is hard for me to believe that a sound like that could be anything but bad news sooner or later," I said.

To hear a cougar scream is a terrifying experience of the first degree. The Monkey showed little concern for the cat, but I was not as convinced as he was that the cougar was harmless.

The beavers were part of our extended family too. They were soon finishing off a second lodge. Recently they added reinforcement to the dam.

"They know exactly how much water should be let through the dam, but I don't know how they get their clues," he said.

The beavers switched their logging operations to the other side of the pond. I think it had something to do with my raids on the alder logs they had felled on our side of the stream.

"Stealing their alder logs worked fine for a short time," I said. "Too bad they got tired of working for us.

"They loved the work. They just didn't like the pay. " The Monkey said.

They didn't seem to mind our presence. They just

kept working away. If we got too close to where they were working we would hear a loud slap of a beaver tail on water, and they would disappear, at least for a short time.

The otters are the funniest in all the animal world. If animals have a sense of humor and stage presence, the otters must be the Lucy's of the forest and stream. The otters know how to enjoy themselves, quite often at the expense of the beavers. For example, while the hard-working beavers are struggling to get a limb from the far end of the pond to the dam, the otters would swim on their backs right alongside the beavers, just to tease them. I have seen an otter ride on the very log that the beaver is trying so hard to move. Whenever they got tired of pestering the beavers they ran to hit their mud slide, which is across the pond from our cave. We had a ring-side seat where we could watch them play on the slide.

"They are competing to see which can slide the farthest into the water without taking a stroke," he said. "Let's cheer and clap and see if we can get them to respond."

It worked. The more we whooped it up the better they performed. They loved the attention. The otters communicate with each other using wailing sounds and grunts. We counted seven distinct sounds

Otters are excellent swimmers and live off the fish they catch, unlike the beavers who eat only vegetation. They kept close track of us and our fishing. When The Monkey fished they would wait until he had caught what they must have figured to be a reasonable number of fish. If he continued fishing, the otters would splash and wail from one end of the pond to the other, under his line, around his bait, and all over. The net result was that the fishing was over for the day. When the otters appeared The Monkey learned that there is no point in contesting them, he just had to wrap up and go home. Interesting, however, they didn't pull that little number when I fished.

The Monkey said, "Your fishing apparently is not seen as a threat by them."

Our pair of Canada geese was a sad love story. The pair, was here when we arrived; however, we did not take note of them until the second week. The hen had a damaged wing that drooped like it was broken. The gander was OK. The gander could have joined up with any one of the many flights of geese that had gone over heading south, but he wouldn't leave his mate.

Our geese would call to the wedges of geese as they passed over. The flying geese would talk back, pleading with our geese to join up. One flight broke formation and circled for about half an hour, but then flew on. Our geese would start flapping in the water and honking long before we could see or hear their friends in flight.

Our gander would encourage the hen to try to fly, and she did try, but she could not. The gander took off several times to follow the other geese, but he would be back in less than an hour. The hen was always so happy to see him return. It was sad to watch them in this struggle.

The Monkey was doubtful whether they would

make it through the winter.

"A fox or something will get the hen," he said.

They finally settled in at the lower end of the beaver pond in some rushes.

The flights of geese have long since ended. I hope they make it through to spring.

In this valley, in this mammoth forest, we are never alone. We have lots of company.

Chapter 14

Food and Fuel

November 30

We were never really going to be "ready" for a hard winter, but even The Monkey thought we were getting to the point where we could "manage." We had accomplished a great deal. The Monkey was still worried about our supply of wood, but as for food he felt we weren't in bad shape.

We had a rock bin two feet by three feet and three feet high, heaped with acorns, and a second one about half full of hazelnuts. The hazelnuts were still in the shells, so the actual amount of food was deceptive. We had stacks of camas paddies or should I say bricks. Camas bulbs and wappato are very much like potatoes, and we have both.

"Camas was a mainstay of the Northwest Indians," he said.

"All I know about camas is that there is a city by that name," I said.

He didn't know that. Camas is a member of the tulip family, *which* means it grows from a bulb—and the bulb had to be dug. Most of the camas or "quamish" as he sometimes called it, grow in the meadows. He wanted to do the camas harvest because he could stay in one general area all day long to work. The soil in the meadow was a soft loam, which made digging the bulbs fairly easy.

But there was another reason he wanted to do the camas harvest. "There are two types of camas," he said. "One camas has a light blue flower and the other one has a white blossom. Other than the differences in color, the plant and bulbs look identical. However, they are quite different in one important way. The ones with white or cream-colored petals are 'death camas.' Eat those bulbs, and it is lights out."

He was serious. The complication came because the white and the blue camas grew together in the same patches. He digs the bulbs with the stem and flower still attached.

"What are you worried about?" I asked. "I'm not color blind."

I didn't feel left out because the wappato harvest was all mine.

"Incidentally," I said, "if you don't know about Camas, Washington, you probably don't know about the city of Wapato, Washington, either." He thought I was putting him on.

"Oh yes, it's right next to Skunk Cabbage, Washington, I bet," he said.

"No, that *is* Camas," I said. If he had ever been downwind from the paper mill in Camas he would have thought my reply was as funny as I did.

He informed me that I could harvest the wappato because it is "squaw" work.

If this guy ever gets out to civilization he will learn about his choice of words the hard way.

When he gave me my instructions on finding wappato I had the distinct feeling I was being sent after a left-handed monkey wrench or perhaps set up for the old snipe hunt ruse. I just listened without saying a word.

"The wappato plant floats on the pond where the water is slack," he said. "The plants are easy to spot because the leaves are so big and shaped like an arrowhead. The tubers or bulbs are in the water. You feel for the tubers with your bare feet. There could be six to ten tubers for each plant, and remember the tubers may not be right under the floating leaves. You pick the tubers off with your toes. When the bulbs float to the top you just scoop them up and put them in the burlap bag that you will tie to your waist. You will soon get the knack of it."

Now, does this sound like a wild goose chase or what?

But he had more."Incidentally," he said, "as long as you are wet, look to see if the yellow pond lily has gone to seed yet. If it has, take a different sack or something to put the seed pods in. The pond lilies are those plants with the large, I mean very large, floating leaves with the yellow flowers. The flowers are six inches wide, or more."

"Maybe I should get one floating plant at a time," I said, and winked at him. He winked back and said, "That's fine."

You can be sure that I waited until he was at the

meadow digging camas before I tried the wappato adventure. By God, it worked. Just the way he said it would. He was not pulling a joke on me after all. The water was cold and the mud oozed between my toes which was creepy, but getting the wappato was worth it.

He was impressed with my harvest of wappato.

"What were you saying about the water lilies?" I asked.

"You mean the yellow pond lilies, " he said, "if they have gone to seed, and they should have by this time, the seeds are found in the middle of the flower in big seed pods. If you like popcorn, you will like this. They say it tastes just like popcorn, so we'll cook it on a sheet of metal over the fire just like you would regular popcorn."

He knew what he was talking about with the wappato, so I figured maybe he wasn't kidding about this poor man's popcorn.

The Monkey converted the pine box that the survival kit came in, to a dried fish larder. The dried fish looks like shingles, and that is the way he stored them, crossing each layer.

He stored each type of meat separately. I never asked him which kind of animal was which. Some meat cures better than others depending on the fat content in the meat and other variables. He said, "There is certain to be spoilage, so by keeping the batches apart it will keep us from losing it all."

The meat, after it is cured, was hung in strips tied together by wire in the back of the cave, as far from the fire as possible.

Gathering wood each day became a bore and was

getting harder to do as we had already cut the most accessible wood out of the logjam. Each day The Monkey insisted that we gather more wood than we would use that night. The additional wood was stacked for later use. We chose as our woodshed the areas just on the other side of the rock walls that formed our living area. This put the wood under cover. We cut each piece of wood in as long a log as he felt I could handle. The bigger in diameter the shorter the log. He did most of the sawing and I did the carrying. His leg was getting much better but he was still afraid to put his full weight on it. *I will carry the wood. I don't mind the work but it is boring.*

The hatchet was put to good use to split off slabs of bark from the old-growth Douglas fir snags in the logjam. The bark was loose, but it had to be split off the logs. We could carry the bark in big slabs because it was so light.

"Pound for pound the bark is our best fuel," he said.

He insisted on storing the bark inside the cave. He stood the slabs of bark against the rock walls of the cave. I objected to this, not that the storage of the bark inside the cave cut our room down too much, because we have lots of room, but because the bark was loaded with ants and I thought perhaps spiders. I asked him for an explanation as to why the bark was not being stored outside with the rest of the wood.

"The layers of bark will form some good natural insulation for the bare rock walls," he said. I understood that concept but I still did not feel that I had received the full answer. I pinned him down more.

He said, "As it is now, we will always have to go outside the cave to get any fuel."

"So what?"I said.

"What if something happened that we could not get out of the cave?" he said.

"Like what? It would sure be some snow storm for it to pile up snow so deep that we couldn't even get out of the cave," I said.

"A snow storm could be one reason," he said. "Especially if we had high winds. I have seen drifts of snow freeze solid as concrete. So drifting snow could strand us inside. However, I doubt that we would be trapped by snow for any great length of time. I'm not too concerned with that."

"I am not letting you out of this conversation that easy," I said. "You said snow could be one reason to be trapped, what else has your cheery mind worried up for us?" I asked.

"Avalanche or mudflows," he said.

There is something about the word avalanche that wakes a person up. It gets your attention.

"What are the chances of something like that happening?" I asked, "Like an avalanche happening," I repeated carefully.

"I have no idea about the chance of an avalanche happening," he said. "We have never been up on top. What the terrain of the mountain above us is like, I couldn't even guess. Avalanches develop for many reasons—such as a high wind after a heavy snow fall and so forth. I can't tell what the history of this valley has been with regard to avalanches, but I can tell you there is a substantial history of mudflows in this valley."

"A mudflow? Are you kidding?" I said. But I knew he wasn't.

"It works like this," he said. "We get a good steady warm rain or a Chinook wind, and that melts the snow pack. No problem with that if the water runs off in nice little natural creek beds. However, it is not uncommon for the creek channels to get plugged up with debris from over the winter. The debris forms a dam which forms a lake. We wouldn't even know that, in fact, a lake was being formed up in the higher reaches of the mountains. The weather could even be very nice down here in the floor of the valley. If the dam gives way under the growing pressure of the newly formed lake, you have a real gusher coming down the mountain and into the valley. A gusher like that can move rocks the size of a car. The soil liquefies and it flows just like a river."

"Does that kind of thing happen often, or is it a once-every-hundred-years sort of thing?" I asked.

He gave it some thought before he answered. "Let me answer your question this way," he said, "how do you think that logjam, which we call our wood pile, got there? If you look up and down the valley, you can see the remains of at least five other such accumulations of logs and rocks. This very cut we live in was caused by water breaking through at some time in the past. All those logjams were once dams holding back quickly formed lakes."

"Maybe you worry too much," I said. "It just seems that we are up against all of nature and we are too small to win them all. There are too many mysteries out there, beyond our little haven, ready to do us in. We have been lucky so far."

He hesitated before he spoke, and I knew I was in for some country philosophy.

"I don't worry," he said, " but I do plan and think a lot. That is different from worrying. If the situation you have thought on never happens, then nothing is lost, unless the thinking gets in the way of something else more important that you should have been doing. Right? Am I right? Do you understand what I am saying?"

I thought I should nod yes to him, and perhaps I could get the whole conversation to end. *Besides, I don't care if there are a few ants or other critters on the bark that he wants to store in the cave.* He read my mind. I knew I had more to hear.

"Take the bark stored in the cave as an example," he said. "The bark will make good insulation. That is a fact. It is also a fact that we have to store it somewhere. It is also a fact that we know that washouts and mudflows have occurred in the past. We don't know about avalanches. With that basic information, if a person did not have a plan he would be ignorant, but if I did not have a plan I would be crazy."

He walked away and I thought we were done, but he was not quite through.

" You said lucky? What is this luck stuff I keep hearing about?" he said. "There is very little luck, good or bad, that you don't make yourself. You speak of the mysteries out there in the woods, of the creek and the mountains. They must all be studied. We need to know more about them. You do that by observation and remembering what we have observed. We use what we think we have learned in a given situation. If it works once, we remember that and test it again. In time the mysteries will become predictable, and then it is no longer a mystery. Now that's not luck." He seemed a little angry and it was obvious that he had given his last word for the night. He went to bed.

I didn't sleep so good. Mudflows and avalanches are not the best thoughts to put a person to sleep.

In the morning I studied the logjam with new interest. I wondered why the log accumulation had stopped where it did. I wouldn't even have thought about the location of the logjam prior to last night's lecture series installment. There had to be a logical explanation for the mudflow and logjam stopping where they did.

I suddenly realized that The Monkey's lecture had sunk in more than I had thought. I was starting to think like he thinks. Before I met this nature boy I would never have thought about such events one way or the other.

I have learned a lot and I .have much more to learn. The Monkey discounts luck. Maybe he is right, but as long as I am stuck in a place like this, it is fortunate, if not lucky, that I am stuck with him instead of the pilot. In fact, to go even farther, if the pilot had any notion of a philosophy like I heard last night from this kid, none of this would have happened in the first place.

Chapter 13

The Bee Tree

November 25

On my trips to gather acorns, I noticed a lot of bee activity in the wild blossoms. I mentioned this to The Monkey.

"If there are bees, shouldn't there be honey?" I asked.

"Right," he said, "the bees are more active because it is the final days of Autumn The bees are putting the last touches on the combs in the hive. All you have to do now is find the bee tree."

"Great, how do I do that?" I asked.

"Bees don't work all that far from their hives, especially if there is plenty near their hive to keep them busy, such as blossoms or ripe fruit. The bees are probably working on the fireweed in the meadow, " he said.

I never know for sure if he makes up the names of the plants and trees or not. The bright red blossoms could be called fireweed.

"Honey is well worth going for," he said.

"That's easy for you to say. You're not the one that is going to get stung," I said. "I am not allergic to bee stings, but I still don't like the prospects of getting stung either."

"You shouldn't get stung by just finding the bee tree," he said. "All you have to do is to be patient and observant, and you will find the hive. Here is what you do…"

The next day broke clear. It was going to be warm again. I waited until the sun was at its highest over the meadow. His comment about my not getting stung by simply locating the hive did not go unnoticed. I was not reassured, because the implication, of course, was that I would get stung later.

I gathered up a supply of fireweed blossoms as he had instructed. I crushed the blossoms until I had a damp sweet-smelling mass of pulp. I laid this pulpy mass over a large exposed boulder in the fireweed patch, and sat down a few feet away. *Here is where the patience part begins,* I thought to myself. But I did not have long to wait. First one, then three, then a dozen or more bees started working the crushed fireweed. They must have thought they were in bee heaven.

"Now the observation part begins," I whispered. Soon a bee, which I had been concentrating on, had gained a full load and flew off. I was up and off in the direction of its flight. But I had gone about fifteen feet when I lost sight of my bee guide.

I crouched down, just as The Monkey had told

me to do, and kept my eyes peeled, watching at the level where I had lost sight of my bee. Within seconds, before I had even become comfortable, I saw another bee fly over. I was up and after it like a shot from a cannon, and promptly tripped over a root. As I picked myself up disappointed that I had lost my prey, I saw the next bee. "Hey, this is fun," I said aloud.

I soon got pretty good at following the bees. It was easy to spot the bees in flight, as opposed to other miscellaneous insects. The bees all flew at about the same height and with a purpose, whereas the other insects wandered or circled with no apparent direction or purpose. I soon perfected a system to trail the bees. I stayed in one place until I lost sight of the critter, then I scurried forward to the last spot that I had visual contact, and sat for a moment waiting to pick up my next guide. In this manner I could watch where I put my feet so I would not trip again. I never had long to wait before another busy bee flew over.

Two hours passed in this fashion. I found myself seldom sitting down now. I just maintained a slow steady pace with a glance up every so often. I knew that all the bees I saw did not come from my crushed fireweed. There was enough bee activity to carry my whole blossom bait away several times over.

I smelled the tree before I located it. The Monkey had said, "You will smell it if it is a big one." He had also told me, "If the hive is in a tree, it will be an oak or maple tree, not a spruce or a fir."

He was right. The bees were in a big leaf maple tree. The hole the bees were going in was about the size of a man's head.

In all it took me about three hours to find the tree, but the distance that I had traveled was not more than three-fourths of a mile. If I had known where to look I could have walked to it in ten to twenty minutes.

I studied the bee tree, making mental notes of all the details that The Monkey had asked for. "How many bees go in? Don't try to count both in and out, just in. Hold your breath and count the bees until you are out of breath," he had said. Well, let's try that. I had lots of breath left but could not keep up with the count. It was too much of a blur around the opening of the hole in the tree. I tried the counting routine several times and gave up. The point of all this counting, as The Monkey explained, was to determine how big the hive was. It was big, if numbers of bees meant anything.

The hole could be reached only if I stood on something. I would have to figure some way to roll a log or a boulder or something up to the base of the tree. I couldn't be expected to stand there on my tip toes and try to raid the hive. I had to think of some way to get higher and closer. The Monkey would have some ideas. He always did.

The Monkey was elated. He pounded me on the back until I ducked.

"Good work. Good work, " he kept saying. "If I had another cigarette darn if I wouldn't give it to you right now."

I thought for a minute that he was going to say "damn." Isn't that interesting though, I hadn't thought that he may have hidden more than one cigarette. What he doesn't know is, smoking is not the incentive for me that it once had been.

"How do we chase the bees away so I don't get stung?" I asked.

"We?" he said. "You mean how do *you* do it." He thought that was funny.

"Well," he said, " there are no guarantees in this hard old world. Often you will find life's greatest gains come right after a person takes a reasonable risk. It is the difficult things in life..."

"Knock off your country bumpkin philosophy, " I said. "What I want to know is am I going to get the crap stung out of me or not?" He hesitated so I went on, "Do we build a fire and smoke them out?" I had heard that some place.

"Smoking them won't work so good in our situation," he said. "If we were able to cut the tree down, smoking might be the answer, but from your description of the size of the tree, that is out."

"So how do we do it?" I asked.

"I guess you will have to do it like a bear would," he said. I didn't like the sound of that at all, but he did not explain any further.

He gave me some relief however, by saying," We won't do anything for now. We will wait until it gets much colder. We need about a week of weather where the temperature does not get above freezing. "Who knows, perhaps by that time I may be able to help you play bear. Anyway we know we got the honey when we want it," he said, " and it is not just the honey, the bee's wax will be very important to us also. There are a thousand uses for the beeswax, not the least of which is that it is very good to chew."

I knew it was a day's work well done.

Do I ever have some stories to tell the friends back home. "Back home," I said aloud to myself. *I don't feel very close to home tonight. In spite of our success today a feeling of loneliness keeps sweeping over me. I must not think of home so much. I will think of other things.* "Honey, " I sighed. *There isn't anything that won't taste better with honey on it. I wonder how much we will get and how we will store it.*

Chapter 15

Gold

December 5

The Monkey was intent on what he was doing. I came up behind him and stood there for several minutes, just watching, before he knew I was there.

"What have you got there that is so... " I never got to finish. He spun around and dropped to one knee, like a wrestler in a defensive stance.

"Don't you ever come up on me like that," he said. "Don't you ever sneak up on me."

It was only the second time I had seen him lose his temper. His eyes were wide with anger, or fear, or both.

"Just hold on a minute, what has gotten into you?" I said. "I don't sneak upon people, on you or anybody else." Now I was angry.

He slumped down to both knees like he had been hit.

"I guess I'm a little spooky. I am sorry," he said. I waved it off, but he could see that I was still perplexed at his outburst.

"I really am sorry," he said. "Sit down. Let me tell you a story."

"Great, I just love story time," I said. He could see that a simple apology was not going to satisfy me. But I did sit down.

"You see," he said, "one of my major responsibilities, which Gramps had given me, was never to let anyone come near us that we didn't already know was around. No one came on to the creek where my Grandfather was working, without my sounding the alarm. OK? And here you walk right up and I didn't know anyone was anywhere around. Tippy always sat looking down the creek and I watched up the creek. No one could get by us."

"Who is Tippy? And what are you talking about?" I asked.

"Tippy was my Australian shepherd, my dog," he said. In a curious way I was relieved. Tippy sounded like a girl's name and I had never heard him mention a girl before.

"Gramps was careful that we did not intrude on anyone else too," he said. "The Murphy Boys had the claim just-down stream from us. We liked the boys. They were good men. Gramps would always holler from the top of the bench in the trail before going slowly on down past their workings. That way by the time we got down to their cabin they would be seated, smoking their pipes, like they had been doing that all day long. They liked us too, but no one could be trusted too far."

He rambled on, and he seemed to have more he wanted to say. I was still not sure what had prompted this flashback.

"What in the hell are you jabbering about?" I finally asked.

"Gold. I'm talking about gold," he said. He said it like anyone would know that.

"I told you Gramps ran a trap line in the winter. Well he did, but his game was gold," he said. "He trapped only when he couldn't prospect or mine. This is what I am talking about."

For the first time I noticed that he had been holding his hand behind his back all the time he was talking to me. He brought his hand around slowly. He had his handkerchief in his hand. He carefully opened the cloth to display a pocket filled with rocks about the size of match heads. The rocks glittered in late fall sunlight.

"Gramps looked all his life and never found anything like this," he said.

"Are you sure?" I asked. "How do you know it's gold? How do you know it is the real thing?" He looked disgusted and took my remarks as a challenge.

"It is the real McCoy alright. I have seen too much of the stuff to make that greenhorn mistake," he said. "I know gold when I see it."

Excitement was creeping over me. "Is it ours? I mean, can we keep it?" I said. I was whispering, as though someone might hear. He laughed and folded his handkerchief up to put it away. I put my hand out to restrain him.

"No, I want to know. How do you know for sure it is gold?" I asked. I tried to make my voice come back to normal. "How do you know it isn't fool's gold or something like that?" I said.

"If you have once seen iron pyrite, or fool's gold, and real gold, you can never be confused again," he said. "What do you know about the properties of gold?" he asked.

"I know it is heavy, it is yellow, and damn hard to get," I said.

"That's pretty good, Sis," he said. "You have said the most significant thing first. Gold is heavy. There are other materials found in nature that are yellow, and iron pyrite is one of them. Mica is another. But gold is the same color of yellowness no matter how you turn it in the light. Iron pyrite will change colors as you turn it in the sunlight. It gives off different colors like turkey feathers do. But you have probably never played with turkey feathers."

"Wrong, I have played with many a turkey," I said. The play on words was lost on my innocent mountain boy.

"But the best test short of a chemical analysis, is to see if it is malleable. Do you understand what I mean?" he asked. He did not give me a chance to reply, which was a relief, because I had only a vague notion of what he was talking about.

"Let me explain," he went on. "Iron pyrite is brittle. It breaks when you put the point of a knife to it. Gold on the other hand, will flatten. Gold is that soft." He had his trusty knife out and placed one of the little shining grains on his forefinger and pressed the blade against it. It cut in half like a hot knife through butter. I could see that one portion was going to fall into the gravel. I made a wild grab for the speck to scoop it up before it hit the ground.

I was not quick enough to save it, but I saw right where it hit in the gravel and concentrated my vision on the spot. My efforts were greeted only with knee slapping and laughter by The Monkey.

"I do believe we have seen the early stages of gold fever," he said. I asked him again, "Is it ours? Is it ours to keep?" He nodded assurance.

"What do we do now?" I said.

"Under different circumstances," he said, "one of us would head to the nearest land office or whatever they call it in Canada, and the other would stay here and ride shotgun. Unless we didn't trust each other, which in that case, we would both go to the land office."

"That's great," I said. "Let me be the one to go to the land office. I will go to town, only which way is it?" We both got a good laugh out of that.

"Where shall I tell them the claim is?" I said as I continued the spoof.

"Tell them it is somewhere east of the Pacific Ocean and north of Vancouver. I think." he said. "If you have to get real specific tell them it is in the mountains. That should pin it down close enough for right now." He was enjoying himself.

He wrapped his newly found wealth in the corner of his handkerchief and started toward the cave.

"How long have you known that there is gold here?" I asked.

"I found colors two days ago when I was getting a drink," he said. "A find of colors didn't surprise me too much. I have seen good-looking quartz in the area. Some nice veins of quartz cross the creek in several places. The gold has been eroded from the veins of quartz over many years; like many thousands of years. I figure that in every high water, such as a spring runoff, this whole delta is covered by water, which has been cutting the veins of quartz. As the water recede it builds up this delta of gold bearing-gravel. I mean this delta we are now standing on."

The delta, as he called it, was a triangular piece of land which fanned out from the water slide.

"The old streambed cut along the far side of the delta," he said. He pointed to the cliff side of the valley. "Sometimes, the successful prospector is the one who can imagine where the water course used to be years ago. Everyone knows where it is today. Look, what I am saying is, the river used to swing way over there against the cliff."

I could clearly see what he meant once he had pointed it out to me.

"Hey, what are we going to the cave for?" I said. "Let's start digging or whatever it is we are supposed to do." I was caught up in this.

"Not so fast, Sis, this is the time to plan and figure out our strategy," he said. "Anyway it is getting late. Let's go back to camp and have that rabbit that has been on the coals all day."

"I can hardly believe my ears," I said. "There must be another hour of daylight left. We could get started digging, or whatever we do to get it. The rabbit can wait. It will be there whenever we get to it."

He said, "I just told you, the delta took thousands of years to form. It will be here tomorrow, the next day, and probably another thousand years or more, but the rabbit is ready to eat now." He was persistent and took me by the arm to steer me toward the cave and that sad-looking roasted rabbit. I talked all the way to camp.

"How much do you think is there?" I asked. "How much is it worth?" "You say we can take it? Let me look at it again."

As I watched him eat, I thought he would never get done chewing the meat off each tiny bone. When he started to top it off with roasted acorns dipped in honey, it was too much. I couldn't contain myself any longer.

"Come on, let's talk." I said. "What do we do first? Do you think there is a lot out there?"

He smoothed off a place in the ashes next to the fire pit. He drew a line with a stick.

"I assume that line represents the present location of the stream," I said. He nodded. He then placed sticks in the shape of the delta, and with a row of rocks for the cliff, he had a good working model.

He said, "It looks like the deposit that formed the delta is about eighteen inches deep at the head and perhaps as deep as three or four feet at the tail end. In each spring runoff the bigger particles of the stuff will drop first and the smaller stuff will continue on further down the delta."

"When you say 'stuff' you do mean gold, don't you?" I asked. He nodded, and continued. "Some of the finer stuff could even reach the end of the delta or fantail. That's where I found this little jag ," he said. "The problem is that gold is so heavy that over a long period of time the better stuff will work downward and lodge against the bedrock. And as I have already said, the bedrock may be eighteen inches to four feet under a lot of overburden. The pay streak (or the real good stuff), may be less than a quarter of an inch thick, right on bedrock. We can't dig that much with our little camp shovel. It would never hold up. " He grew quiet.

"The water could be our shovel, our tool, I think," I offered.

He turned and looked at me, a little surprise registered on his face. "I think you are on to something," he said, "what are you thinking?"

"I don't know for sure, but if we could get a small stream to cut the delta, perhaps it would move some of what you called the overburden," I said.

"If we had power for a pump, and a hose and nozzle, we could cut the delta in half easily," he said, "but I don't see how we can use the water if we can't harness it." He went back to thinking.

"The only way I can contribute to this process is if you talk," I said. "I can't be of much help if you only think to yourself. So if you had a pressure hose, where would you start?"

"I have been trying to think what Gramps would do," he said. "I think he would start right at the creek side and move the tailings, or waste material, into the creek to be carried away."

"But the way you described it earlier it would seem to me that the coarser gold would be where the delta meets the cliff wall and down that line to bedrock," I said. I pointed to the rock in his model to make my point clear. He looked pleased.

"That's correct," he said, "but you have to move the tailings someplace to work across the delta to get to the cliff. That's why Gramps would start on the creek side of the delta. You have to be able to move the tailings." There was another long silence, which I broke again.

"But your Grandfather would plot out a scheme that could take several years," I said. "He would know that by working methodically he would eventually arrive at the cliff, because he would have lots of time. We have to get to the bedrock at the base of the cliff rather soon. We don't have the time. We don't have too much more time until things freeze up around here. We might have a little time in the spring but if the weather is good enough for mining, it would be good enough walking out. Right?"

"You have a point there, he said. "However, at the time we made our plan to walk out in the spring, we didn't know we would find gold. If we could develop a good method to get the overburden off, a full year's work in here could prove interesting."

"Interesting?" I said. I stopped stoking the fire and turned toward him so he could get the full impact of what I was about to say.

"You accused me of an early dose of gold fever. Well, you have gone beyond fever, you have the sickness," I said. "Hear me carefully when I say, I want to go home. At first, I doubted if I would ever see my family again, but now, thanks to you, to your experience and planning and your sheer display of guts, I am convinced that at least we have a chance to make it out. So, when the weather permits in the spring, I say we should stick with our plan and walk out. I don't want to go without you, but I will. I am leaving and all the gold in the world won't stop me. I want to see my family, I want a hot shower, and I want some food that isn't burned or smells like alder wood." I was finished with my speech.

A slow grin came over his face. He got up slowly to his feet and walked around to my side of the fire. As he approached, he stuck out his hand

"We are partners," he said, "and partners do things together."

I was relieved. I mean really relieved.

The Monkey had a little more he wanted to say. "You couldn't have said it any better. Gold will sometimes twist your thinking. It can even change a person's personality," he said. "You bet we are going home. You to your old home, and me? I guess to a new one. They didn't make enough gold to change that. And while we are here, our priorities are still the same, keeping warm, keeping fed, and keeping safe. After all of that is taken care of, and only then, we will do our digging. If it is not that way, we won't live to enjoy the gold anyway. Besides, I may have all the gold there is, inside that knot in my handkerchief."

"Thank you. I feel much better now," I said, "but on one point, I don't believe you have all the gold in the creek rounded up and I don't think you believe you do either."

"Yep, partner, you are right, there is more gold. In substantial amounts I think." All this time he had been shaking and squeezing my hand. This new partnership was hard on the hand.

"Sit down partner, and give me back what is left of my hand," I said.

We sat on a log together looking into the fire in silence, once again. I put my arm around his shoulder in a partner-like fashion. I asked him, "If we are real mining partners, shouldn't we have a paper or something written up, and shouldn't we both sign it?"

"You bet," he said. "Write it up, but remember that it will only be a paper. Our handshake is the real binder and we have already shaken hands on it, right?"

Did we ever! My hand still smarted. It was nice to sit in the warmth from the fire with my arm around his shoulder. A person could do worse for a partner.

He told me stories about his grandfather and their claim and how they had worked it together. I was beginning to feel like I knew Gramps myself. He must have been a character. The Monkey never mentioned his father and only a little about his mother, and nothing at all about anyone else.

"Do you know it will be light in another hour?" he finally said. "We have talked the night away."

"I'm not tired," I said.

"You will be, "he said. "Let's get some shut eye. I think tomorrow will be a good day. Good night, Sis." With that he rolled up in his mats.

"Good night, partner," I said. Then as an after thought I told him, "I'm glad we are partners." He didn't hear me. He was already asleep.

Chapter 16

Engineering Problems

December 6

Although we had not had much sleep we were up at the first scolding of the blue jays. There was a portion of the rabbit to finish off for breakfast.

"I'm headed out to check the snares," he said. "Why don't you try for a mess of fish, just in case the snares are empty." He added a good supply of wood to the embers in the fire pit. "The fire will be down to coals by the time either of us gets back. Whoever gets here first can put their game in the pit to roast for supper," he said. "I will meet you at the base of the water slide when the sun is at its highest."

With that and a handful of acorns he was gone.

I was at the water slide before he got there. I had picked up the camp shovel and brought it with me.

"Trying a little digging I see," he said.

"Enough to see that you are right about not being able to remove much overburden with this shovel," I said, "but I do have another idea."

"Shoot, what is the idea?" he asked.

"I still think that the water is the answer to mov-

ing the unwanted rubble off the top of the ground,"
I said.

"Say some more."

"If we could get a little trench dug so the water
would run into a little canal, wouldn't that carry the
silt further down the delta?" I suggested. "As the
channel is cut deeper by the running water, it would,
in time, cut a path to the bedrock, wouldn't it?" I
hurried on to explain my concept. "If we could get a
trickle started, I am sure it would work," I said.

"Your idea is a good one, Sis. It would work,
only how do we get the water into the trench in the
first-place?" he said.

I had more to my plan but I was reluctant to go
further because the idea could be dumb. He walked
up and down the delta to look the situation over.
Finally, he came back to the edge of the splash pond
where the water from the slide emptied. I was
nonchalantly throwing rocks into the water.

"There is enough fall to make your idea work,"
he said. "The head of the delta is a good six feet
higher than the tail end. So we have the slope or fall.
That's good, but that still does not get the water into
a trench. I have thought about a siphon, but I can't
think of anything we have that would work as a siphon. I have considered a flume, and that may still
be our best bet. We would make it out of logs I suppose. We would use cedar, and split the logs some
way—and then hollow them out by burning, like
the Indians used to do to make their dugout canoes.
It would take forever..."

I interrupted him. It was time to give him all of

my idea. It wouldn't be any dumber than the ideas I had just heard from him.

"Are you missing the whole point?" I didn't give him time to reply, but rushed right on. "You said that spring runoffs most likely made this delta. I propose that we make our own spring runoff."

"Keep talking," he said.

"If we could dam the creek where the water runs out of the splash basin, we could raise the level of the water in the pool until eventually our trench would be the low spot, and the water would escape there. With a little assistance we could get a trickle started. We would only have to raise the water in the splash pool about six inches, and it would be high enough to work. We have lots of river rock which we could use to form the dam. All we have to do is throw rock in a line across the outlet of the pond. It would work, I know it would work," I said. I had pleaded my case with the excitement building in me. He had let me keep on selling my idea long after he had apparently already made up his mind that I was on to something good.

"In fact you are so sure it will work that you have already started on the dam, judging from the mound of rocks I see in an amazingly straight line across the creek," he said.

"You bet, I have started the dam and look at my stakes showing the water level," I said. "See how much the pond has risen already?" I didn't want it to sound like I was bragging, but it was really working.

"There is only one small improvement I can see to your scheme," he said, "and that is not to cut the trench all the way through to the pond. We will leave a barrier that we will cut out at the last minute. That way we won't have a mere trickle going down our canal, we will have a full bore gusher. A spring run-off gusher. Remember, if you double the velocity of water, it increases the carrying power four-fold. So if we double the size of the gusher it will cut four times as fast, or if we triple the speed..."

He had never said anything about the carrying power of water. If he had, I think I would have re-membered it. I have no way of knowing whether what he says is right or not, but it sounds very sci-entific. I should have come right back and said, "Oh, I thought it was six fold. I'm sure you said sixfold," just to see what he would have said.

"Let's give it a try," he said. "You continue to throw rocks to make the dam higher and I will scratch a shallow channel down the middle of the delta. Let's see how far a gusher will go."

It was getting dark, but I had a respectable dam in place. The water level in the splash pool had raised about ten inches. That is a lot of water. It looked like the level of the water was about six inches above the level of the opening to the trench. The channel he had made ran about one-fifth of the way to the end of the delta.

"Let's give her a try," he said. With several deft drags of the camp shovel he broke through the bar-rier between the trench and the pond.

It worked like a charm. The water rushed into our ditch and roared along the course set for it, to our cheering and clapping. The major thrust of the water was over quite soon, but the ditch was now a gully twice the width and at least three times deeper than the trench had been. We squealed like little kids as we watched the running water do in minutes what it would have taken us hours to have done by hand.

When the water had slowed to a trickle, The Monkey started to fill the gap between the trench and the pond with rocks and loose material to form a new barrier.

"By morning," he said, "the level of the water in the pond will be more than high enough to do it all over again. We may make a few alterations each time, but the system will work. We will soon have a cross-cut of the delta."

The next morning The Monkey put a new woven cedar mat in the bottom of the ditch at the point where the water first began to slow down.

"Might as well trap any of the finer stuff, if there is any," he said.

This began to be a daily routine for him. After the main rush of water was past each time, he would carefully roll up the cedar mat and carry it up to the camp where he would unroll the mat to let it dry. At night by the light of the fire he would shake the black sandy material out on the small canvas tarp and then go to work, methodically picking the "good" stuff out of the sand. He would dampen his forefinger and dab at the specks he spotted. His moist fingertip would pick up black sand as well as the flake of gold he was after. Next, he would dip his finger into a clay pinch pot of water and off would come sand and gold into the pot. With a little practice I myself even became quite proficient at this.

We tried not to let our little mining operation intrude too much into our regular activities of gathering wood or food preparations, but nevertheless the mining did consume our time.

We flushed the channel at least twice a day, and though we could leave the workings to go do other things, we found ourselves watching the water rush each time until the water slacked. In less than a week the ditch was down nearly to bedrock at the upper end, and it extended the full length of the delta.

In the second week of the operation, the particles of gold recovered in the cedar mat took an interesting turn. From small perfectly round flakes, the particles of gold became irregular flakes, then became tiny cubes, and then we saw larger pieces the size of match heads. On occasion we would find a piece that he said was large enough to be called a nugget. The Monkey pointed these changes out to me. He had placed flakes under the lens we had acquired in the survival kit, so he was aware of the changing shapes.

"What does it mean?" I asked.

"The flatter the flakes and the more rounded they are, this indicates that they have been carried farther from the vein from which they were cut," he said. "In other words when the flakes are round and thin it's because they have been beaten thin. Prospectors like to see the cubes because they know they are near the lode."

Our excitement over the increasing size of the flakes was short-lived. Within the span of three more flushes, the amount of gold didn't slow down, it ended. I mean it flat out stopped altogether.

"I don't know what to make of it," The Monkey said. "I understand why the particles were getting larger after each flush. It was because the lighter and smaller stuff would not be as deep as the bigger and heavier stuff, and the flushes were reaching the finer flakes first. But the channel is still not cut all the way to bedrock, so you wouldn't expect the gold to peter out until after we reached that point."

"Are you concerned?" I asked.

"Yes and no," he said, "I am concerned that I don't have an answer for the fact that the gold is gone, but I am not too concerned, because we will just move our ditch over a few yards, and start another crosscut. There is plenty of room to start and run a good many more ditches through the delta. It is interesting, however, that we ran dry of gold before we should have ... There is a reason. Tomorrow we will move over about fifteen feet and start a new ditch."

December 18

He was up the next morning early, even for him. He moved quietly around the camp, but I was awake. I thought it was curious that he did not start stirring up the coals of the previous evening fire, as was his custom. It was just too early for me, so I drifted back to sleep. I woke up again to the breaking of small branches he was feeding into the morning fire.

"Where have you been?" I said.

"I got to thinking about the gold drying up the way it did and I developed a theory that I needed to test," he said.

"Am I going to hear the theory?" I said.

"Can you remember what I told you was the first principle in finding gold?" he asked.

I did remember and recited it for him. "You said, remember gold is heavy. Think 'heavy ' you told me."

"Correct, Sis. Now listen to this. What if the gold in the channel was too big and too heavy to be moved by our flushing scheme? I got to thinking about a dredge operation that Gramps had worked on at one time in the state of Washington, at a place called Swauk Creek."

"I'm from Washington. I never heard of a place called that," I said. I had hoped that he would sense that it was a bit early in the morning for tales from his grandfather. No such luck. I was going to hear about Swauk Creek whether I wanted to or not.

"Anyway the dredge," he said, "had worked out this area of the creek. There is a screen on a dredge that keeps the larger rocks out, and this material is carried away on a conveyor belt to be dumped on the tailings pile. That way only the material that can go through the screen is processed. Do you get the picture? Well, so years later someone found out that the stuff too big to go through the screen was actually gold nuggets. They were throwing away the best stuff." He broke into laughter, just the way I suppose his grandfather had laughed every time he had told the story, which was probably too often.

When his laughing had subsided, he took out his. trusty handkerchief and opened it for me to see the contents. I know my eyes must have popped right out of their sockets. I sputtered and gasped several times.

"My God, look what you have," I said. He had nuggets the size of a thumbnail and larger. "My God," I said again.

"I found these in about twenty minutes of picking in the bottom of the ditch," he said. "When the sun is higher so we can see into the bottom better, it will be fun. We have a real bonanza here."

It was a fast breakfast. We were down in the channel, sunlight or not. We stopped often to show each other our most recent finds. The sun was low in a heavy sky before we stopped to survey our triumphs.

"I noticed that putting wood gathering aside for serious prospecting wasn't too hard for you," I said.

"I have to admit you are right," he said, "but I don't feel too guilty about the time we have spent, because this is our last day. We wrap it up today."

I was all set to explode with laughter but suppressed it as I saw he was not trying to be funny. "But I haven't finished by any means," I said. I know I was stammering and sputtering.

"No, this is it, Sis, our Indian summer is over. There was ice again on the beaver pond this morning, and it looks like the rain will be returning soon. We are out of time, but more to the point, we are getting too much," he said.

"Too much? How do you get too much gold?" I said.

"Think about it," he said. "None of it will do us any good if we can't spend it, right? The way we are going we will have to leave food and other necessities behind for the sake of the gold. Isn't there a story about someone who drowned because they wouldn't empty their pockets of silver coins?"

"You probably made up that story," I said, "but I get the point."

"What will this buy?" he asked. "I know about how much we have in terms of ounces, but I have no idea what it will buy," he said.

"You said gold was worth over four hundred dollars an ounce and there are sixteen ounces in a pound, so...."

"No," he said, "there are twelve ounces to a pound, and I can figure all of that. What I want to know is what will it buy? Could I rent a place to live, things like that?"

"We don't have to argue the facts now but there are sixteen ounces in a pound," I said. I could see that he was not going to let go of it.

"Not when you are talking about gold. When it is gold it is twelve ounces," he said.

"Who gives a damn," I said. "If we packed out twenty pounds a piece, we could buy a hell of a lot, I do know that."

"Too much, too much," he said, "perhaps four to five pounds each, but that is it."

He made it sound like the final word but we will see when the time comes.

We did close down the gold mining operation the next day. When we had finished, little could be seen to ever indicate what we had done at this spot. Removing the dam was not nearly as much fun as putting it in. It started to rain hard before we were done. It was a bone-chilling rain and the fire was welcomed more than usual this evening.

We went to bed hungry because we had not snared or fished in several days. We could have done quite well on acorns or hazelnuts I thought, but he never mentioned it. I think it was his form of self-punishment for his unfaithful attention to the basics because he had let gold get in the way of things that really matter, like food.

Chapter 17

If It Be Thy Will

December 19

I t had snowed several times over the past few weeks, but it turned to rain each time, and was gone in a few hours. This storm started off differently and we knew it. The ground was frozen solid so any snow that fell was going to stick. We felt the temperature dropping by mid-day. Darkness would come early tonight.

It started to snow in earnest about three o'clock. The Monkey came in early from the snare lines. He reported a good day of snaring. He had two rabbits and a quail to show for his efforts.

"More snares were tripped," he said, "but they were empty." We both had observed an increased level of small game activity.

"They all know that a storm is about to hit," he said.

The Monkey built the fire larger than usual and I was glad. We ate early because it seemed so late. After our meal and when chores were done, we stood in the doorway of our cave and watched in silence while the snow came down. The air was still, not even a light breeze was blowing.

"In another setting," I said, "this would be a beautiful sight."

"How could there be a prettier setting?" he said.

"You know what I mean," I said, "with friends, with popcorn, and sleds, and things like that. Like if we were home." He looked at me and was going to say something but he remained silent. I had forgotten what different frames of reference we had. My comments were insensitive.

"I am sorry to have mentioned my home," I said.

He shrugged it off. "There is no need to apologize for saying what you think and feel," he said.

"But it was mean of me to bring up something that you have never known," I said.

"It wasn't mean, if you didn't do it to be mean," he said, "but don't think for a moment that I didn't have a home. And quite frankly it may surprise you to learn that I am not envious of you. My Gramps and my dog and our cabin was the home I remember. Our home was different, but don't think I didn't have a home. Oh yes, I had a home—and I miss it the same way as you miss yours. The main difference as I see it, is that my home, the one I remember, is in the past—and yours is in the present and the future."

His attempt to relieve my guilt did not work, but I appreciated his efforts. I have to admit I was curious to know more about his background. I decided to try to pry his door of privacy open a little further. "Can you remember the years before you went to stay with your Grandfather?" I asked. "Can you remember your mother at all?" I first was glad I had asked the question, yet suddenly I wished I hadn't. Either he would feel comfortable and talk, or he wouldn't. I decided I would just accept it if he preferred to remain private.

He went to the opening again, I presume to watch the snow pile up. I joined him.

"Sometimes I think I can remember my mother, but I'm not sure," he finally said. "When I was sent away I know I was young enough to fly free. I have heard that story plenty of times. My mother had married into the McDowells who I guess were all high graders."

"High graders?" I said.

"Thieves. Gramps was glad to get me and I know he wanted my mother to come north too, but she didn't."

"She probably couldn't," I said.

"My mother was the light of Gramps' life," he said. "To some extent he transferred that role to me."

"Is your mother still alive?" I asked. He didn't seem to mind my questions, but I was watching for any flash point.

"No, I'm sure she is not. Gramps was certain something had happened to her. Otherwise she would have come for me, or she would have gotten some word to us, wouldn't she?" he said.

That was a tough question and I wasn't going to speculate on it. In any case he continued right on without noticing that I had not answered his question.

"Gramps was always repeating something that mom had said as a girl, or telling about some little trick she had pulled," he said. "It used to make me feel good when he would tell those stories about her. I knew he thought she was something special."

He seemed lost in thought and I figured the conversation had ended for the night. But after a long pause he continued.

"Besides the loss of Gramps and Tippy, the saddest thing about the cabin fire was the loss of some pictures Gramps had of Mom and some other folks," he said. "I would have liked to have kept that connection, but all that is in the past now."

"Do you remember the fire?" I ventured. He looked at me with a flash of anger, or it may have been something else. When he started to talk again his voice was very low, but not exactly as if he were angry.

"I wasn't there when the cabin burned," he said. "I had decided to take that day to hike to a highland lake to try some fishing. I saw the smoke from the crest of the pass. The cabin burned to the ground with both Gramps and Tippy inside."

I didn't want to interrupt his story. He was telling me more than I had expected he would. But I had to say, "It is strange that the dog didn't get out, even if your Grandfather was not able too."

"The whole thing was more than strange," he said. "Tippy was never permitted in the cabin except in the case of a blizzard and that was rare. She was an outdoors dog. And I can't imagine Gramps being in the cabin in the middle of the day when there was work to be done."

"Do you blame yourself for not being there?" I said.

"Do I feel guilty or something? No, not really. If I would have been there I think there would just have been one more corpse," he said. "The Murphy Boys arrived shortly after I did. They had seen the smoke too."

I had to ask the obvious question. "Could it have been foul play ? Could the Murphys have had anything to do with it? Did the authorities investigate?"

"I am convinced that the Murphys had nothing to do with the fire. There would have been no purpose to it. I do think they had a theory about it, however, that they never shared with me. I knew they thought there was something strange about the fire. I stayed the next week after the fire with the Murphy Boys. They carried their rifles with them every place they went, and I had never seen them do that before. As to whether it was ever investigated or not; who is going to investigate the death of an old miner who died thirty miles from the nearest official? I have my own theories which I will test someday. Gramps deserves that much."

It was impossible to see more than a few feet into the night because the light from the fire reflected against the falling snow. It was falling even harder, if that is possible. We stood and watched in silence until a small pitch explosion and a shower of sparks in the firepit brought us back to our present world.

From out of nowhere The Monkey said,
> "The snow had begun in the gloaming,
> And busily through the night,
> Had covered the fields and highways,
> With a stillness deep and white."

"Where did you get that? That is beautiful," I said.

"That was something Gramps would always say

at the beginning of a major snow storm," he said. "It is from a poem he liked. It was as if he wanted to verify that yes, this is a big one."

The chill of the night sent us back to the fireside. In the hush that settled over the whole world, thoughts of my own childhood came to my mind. I remembered when I looked forward to, and even longed for storms like this, because they represented no threat or worry only fun.

"Well we can sleep in, in the morning. There will be no school tomorrow," I said. I pretended to turn off the T.V. set.

"What? What did you say?" he asked.

"Oh, nothing," I said, "I was just thinking out loud."

He put an extra log on the fire and retired to his own corner as I did to mine.

By mid-morning the next day the sky had become lighter. About sixteen inches of snow had fallen. I would have guessed that there would have been much more snow on the ground, but the snow was as fine as sugar.

By early afternoon the sky became completely white again and it began to snow once more. The snow had lost its beauty to me as the practical aspects of a deep snow started to creep into my mind. The hours and hours of food preparation and wood gathering that The Monkey had insisted upon had suddenly increased in significance.

"What if this lasted a long time?" I asked. "Do we have enough food do you think?"

"To answer your first question," he said, " I expect there will be snow on the ground until spring.

We are in the mountains, but beyond that, we are on the western slope of the mountain range. So every storm that drives in from the Pacific Ocean will dump its load on this side as the clouds raise to push over the mountains. Will we have enough food, and, I would add, fuel? I would say we can't live exclusively off our stores without some replenishment. Fishing is not entirely out, if we do it right. The fish's food supply will be reduced. They will be plenty hungry if we can get a hook and bait to them."

He continued the assessment of our situation. "In some ways getting meat will be easier with snow on the ground," he said. "The animals travel less, they must take more chances, and it is impossible for them to hide their favorite routes. They will become more desperate as the winter sinks deeper. The animals will have to adjust or die, and so will we. If this snow continues, it will be an ideal time to try for the deer."

"Do we have to kill the deer family?" I said.

"That depends, I guess. But we will be lucky if the question isn't settled for us by the cat anyway," he said.

"What cat?" I said.

"The cougar that we have heard screaming off and on all fall. The same one that has left his tracks around the camp here," he said.

That was the first time I had heard that. "Are you kidding me again?" I asked.

"Nothing to worry about, Sis," he said, "he has us all cased out. He is very curious but he won't take us on. I don't think."

I was still not sure I should take this all in or not.

"Have you actually seen a cougar?" I asked.

"No, I haven't seen him," he said. "I would give my eye teeth to see him. But we have heard him, and I have seen his tracks. The day that we had the first heavy frost he followed your tracks across the creek and up under the oak trees where you were picking acorns."

"He what!" I said. I could feel the hair, on the back of my neck stand straight up.

"He was just curious, so I didn't see any reason to mention it at the time," he said.

He had me going and he was enjoying every minute of it.

"You didn't say anything because you knew if I knew, then I would never go after acorns again," I said. "Why did he follow me if he had already 'cased us out' as you describe it?"

"He wanted to see if you were marking territory," he said. "You weren't. So he did. He sprayed three old snags real good and then flaunted it by stepping right on top of your boot tracks for at least a quarter of a mile. He satisfied his curiosity and felt secure that you were not after his area, so he turned at right angles to your trail and went up the other side of the canyon from you. I think his area is generally across the canyon. But as the snow gets deeper he will have to range a little wider for food. That food will be deer. Which means he already has our little deer family in the back of his mind. Say Sis, you didn't did you?" he said.

"Didn't what?"

"You didn't do any marking up there, did you?" he said.

He tried to appear serious but his grin gave him

away. I pretended right back that I was shocked.

"If marking means what I think it does, it is none of your business," I said, "but no I didn't." For the first time I began to think that he was not quite as innocent as he appeared.

The snow continued to fall with an accumulation of over two feet by the next day. We didn't try to go out much, but busied ourselves around the camp. Some chores had backed up on us and I was glad to be busy.

The Monkey seemed to be enjoying himself but soon I was depressed.

"What is eating you, Sis," he asked. "This won't be so bad. We are fairly well fixed for a long haul."

"I guess in the back of my mind I never accepted that we wouldn't be rescued. I always thought that someone would find us sooner or later," I said. "Even all the time we were preparing to spend the winter, I guess I really didn't think it would happen. I agreed with your logic that no one would find us, but until now, until this snow storm, I still thought someone could have found us. Now how could anyone get to us? We are stranded here until the snow melts, aren't we?" My question really wasn't a question—more of a statement.

"You have known that fact for a long time," he said. "That's why we worked so hard to prepare for this, and there is more we can do. It will get worse before it gets better."

I didn't find much reassurance in his words at all. My depression only deepened. I thought, *who are we trying to kid? We are going to die right here. I wonder if it is better to freeze to death or to starve to death. I had never thought much about death, not even when I knew the plane was going to crash. I was thinking about death now, however. Our lives may be measured in mere days for all I know.*

For the first time in my life I wished I had a better understanding of some religion. This would be the time to pray. Hell, I've never prayed. I wouldn't even know how to pray. We should have at least tried to make it out before the snow fell. With the long Indian summer we had, we might have made it. We are not going to survive here until spring. That just isn't realistic. I will never see my family or friends again—and I don't even know the name of this place.

And then a strange thing happened. It was as if he could read my mind. He came over to where I was hunched up by the fire. He knelt down and awk-wardly patted me on the shoulder. His voice was low and calm.

"You are going to make it out. We will make it out together," he said. "We will make it out because we will never quit. We will not give up, no matter what."

He kept talking softly to me.

"You have so *much* to live for," he said, "and I promise you, you will see and laugh with your friends again, I promise you."

His next comment was so uncanny that I won-dered if he was some kind of a psychic. Out of the blue he said, "One time I asked my Gramps to teach me to pray." He waited to allow me my usual smart remark about his story telling, but I did not say a word.

"I had heard Gramps say something low to himself each night before he went to sleep," he said. "I asked him if he would teach me to do that. I could see that whatever it was he said, it let him go right to sleep afterwards. I had been having some night-mares and I wanted to go to sleep like he did."

"He told me that no one had to be taught to pray. That all you do is talk to God. Talk to Him a little bit and tell Him what's worrying you. He will always listen to you. Gramps asked me if I thought I under-stood. I nodded that I did, but to tell you the truth, I wasn't sure that there wasn't something special you had to say, or something you were supposed to do. So I listened to Gramps for several nights. We slept in the same bed, which I suppose seems funny to you. I listened with all my might. I held my breath so I could hear better. It was almost like spying on my own Grandfather. But I really wanted to learn to pray and do it right.

"I could hear how he started his prayer, but after that, he talked so softly I could not make out what he was saying. He always started the same—but the words in the middle, were never the same. Then he would end up louder, and I could pick that up. At the end he always would say, 'Amen'. I asked him what Amen meant. He told me it just means 'the end,' and 'thank you for listening.'

"So I learned that you have to get God's atten-tion in a certain way, then you talk to Him a bit, and then you say, 'Amen,' to let Him know you're done."

"I started talking to God each night the same way Gramps did. It made me feel so much better. I never had another nightmare to this day. Now, I don't think I could go to sleep without talking to God a bit. I call it praying."

He stopped to stir the fire. I had no comment to make. I had no voice that I could make work.

He said, "You know it seems like I can still smell Gramps. His tobacco and his sweat were so comforting. Yea, Sis, we will make it out if we do all we can to help ourselves, because I know that Gramps and God are pulling for us. It has been the things that Gramps taught me that has fed and warmed us so far. Somebody taught Gramps, probably his dad, and so on, till it gets all the way back to God."

Then with what appeared to be an afterthought The Monkey said, "Sis, I say your name to God when I talk to Him, so He has heard of you."

He was so serious that I started to laugh—and he joined me. If that cougar was out there listening he would have thought we had both flipped our lids. We laughed until the tears came.

"So God has heard of me," I said. And we both started to laugh again.

After stoking the fire one more time The Monkey removed himself to his side of the cave. "Hey Monkey," I said, "how did your Gramps begin his prayers? You never said."

"You mean what did he say at the beginning each time?" he asked.

He knew damn well what I meant. He waited a long time to reply. I was just about ready to ask him again when The Monkey said, "It went like this. 'Dear Lord, if it be Thy will...'"

His voice trailed off too low for me to hear what he was saying, but I am sure I heard "Sis" and then later a clear and loud, "Amen."

I think he was asleep within a minute.

I turned in after checking the weather again. I lay there thinking over the evening.

"Dear Lord, if it be Thy will please help us to make it through till spring. Amen."

I must have gone right to sleep because the next thing I knew was the sound of the morning fire and breakfast under way.

Chapter 18

A Stitch In Time

December 21

To be snowed in for a few days did not bother The Monkey. He busied himself with his sewing. Almost from the time of the crash, The Monkey was making something to wear or to cover us. I have not made enough notes on these efforts. I fondly appreciated that during the the first days of our stay under the roots of the wind-throw he wove cedar blankets to give us some cover at night. Those woven blankets were so effective in our first days and nights.

After I had cannibalized the airplane he had lots of material to work with, plus he had needles and thread. One of his early efforts was to make over-shoes for me. He really had a hang-up on shoes. He was recuperating with broken and bruised legs so he did not concern himself so much with his own shoes.

At the time of the crash I had my eighty-five-dollar Nikes on. He could see that they were well- fitted and comfortable, but he knew they would never last through the months ahead of us. The strategy he sold me on was to protect my existing shoes rather than let them wear out, which would force me to replace them altogether. The method used was to wear a series of overshoes.

The first pair of overshoes he made were from the seat covers from the plane. They lasted less than a day in the rain. He went next to the sun visors from the plane, which he cut in the shape of the soles of my feet. They worked a little better, but they caused me to stumble too much. The Monkey was afraid to continue allowing me to wear them.

The first skins that were cured and dried were rabbit skins, which went into footgear for me. These rabbit boots looked like large socks which tied around my ankles. They lasted a long time because I could turn them so that different parts of the socks came in contact with the ground.

As a consequence of these efforts my original shoes showed little wear. I wouldn't say they were as good as new, but almost. All this work to preserve my shoes would have been a good commercial for Nike.

The Monkey was better off in terms of foot gear. At the time of the crash he had a good grade of leather high-top boots, and the pilot's oxfords fit him. This surprised me, but The Monkey had big feet. He was going to be tall someday. Not that he is short now. Anyway, he had two pairs of shoes from the start. However, he still made himself a pair of boot socks too.

He was a master in the use of cedar bark for a variety of clothing. Some of it I have already written about. He made a cone-shaped hat out of cedar bark that shed rain like the back of a duck. The hat was very light, which was a disadvantage in any wind. He fashioned chin-straps to counteract the wind but they still did not work very well. The wind would either tip the hat so you couldn't see, or tip it back and bare your head. In straight rain, however, the hats worked great, and we did have many days of "straight" rain with no wind at all.

He made ponchos out of cedar bark that hung to the ground. The design was like a sandwich billboard, with the hinges at the shoulders. There were slits for the arms that gave us full range and use of our arms. After we acquired beeswax he improved the ponchos by waxing the shoulder seams, which made the outfit practically waterproof. With our ponchos and cedar dunce caps on, we were a classic of camouflage in the fall and early winter, but once it began to snow we stood out against the snow-covered ground like a sore thumb.

He made skull caps from the headliner in the plane. We used these caps as sleeping caps. He carefully went through a long explanation of how much heat was lost through the top of your head.

"If your feet are cold, put something on your head," he said.

One of the most welcome items as far as I was concerned was also made from the headliner material. That was what he called our "sleeping socks." The night socks were big and loose, and came up over my knees when I was in bed.

He also made a full head hat with ear flaps that tied down over our ears, or they could be tied up on top when the sun was out. These hats were made with the fur side in, and they were warm. At first the smell of wet and not so well-cured fur bothered me. I would take a deep breath of fresh air and quickly put my hat on. On wet or warm days the fur got pretty rank.

I had found one leather glove in the plane. I never found the other one. The Monkey cut the seams of the glove and took it apart to be used as a pattern. It worked well, but I still liked the mittens he made better.

The mittens kept my hands warmer, but if a person had to use his fingers he had to take the mittens off. To help this situation he made one mitten for my left hand and a fingered glove for my right hand. It looked strange but it is a good idea.

The artistic furrier award, however, would go to the raccoon capes he made. We wore the capes over our shoulders in the evenings around the fire. We turned the cape to the side that was turned away from the fire. When we faced the fire to get our fronts warm, the cape would be in its normal position around our backs and shoulders. As we turned to warm our backs we swiveled the cape to our front or chest side. It was keen.

"We will use every bit of leather and fur in some manner," he said. I believe he did too. He cut narrow strips of leather that he dipped in beeswax for the laces.

"The beeswax not only waterproofs the laces, but it also makes them much stronger," he explained.

Beeswax has many uses in making clothing. It is good for waterproofing seams, it makes clothing stronger, and it makes leather more pliable. We chewed the beeswax as chewing gum. We not only got some nourishment from the honey still in the wax, but at the same time it was also preparing the wax for other uses.

The Monkey spent a few minutes of every evening to fashion, repair, or sew some item of clothing. I became quite good at braiding and weaving but I never got the hang of cutting items out of leather.

His major failure, I suppose, was his snow shoes. He tried several designs but none of them was very successful.

"We need something to keep us on the top of the snow. Otherwise our routes will be greatly restricted," he said.

He is working on another concept now. A snowshoe shouldn't be that hard to make.

Many of his items look funny, and would not do well in an Easter Parade but they are functional, and for us, that is what counts.

I laughed, "One good thing about it is that I don't have to spend much time each morning selecting my wardrobe of the day. And color coordination is not much of a problem either."

Thank God, no one can smell me but The Monkey, and since he is no gardenia patch himself, we get along fine.

Chapter 19

Repayment

December 22

You have asked me several times, after I have made you something, or did some thing for you, what you could do for me," he said.

As a matter of fact it seemed like he was always fixing something for me. I had mentioned several times that I wished I wasn't so helpless in some of these tasks.

"Any thing I have made for you was usually for my benefit as well," he said. "I have never figured you owe me anything. I just did what I should, and if it turned out OK, then that is good. A person doesn't need to be paid back for doing what they should do anyway."

"Stop beating around the bush," I said. "I obviously have something you want. Whatever I can give you I will—well, almost anything."

He said, "Every night you write in your note-book."

"What about it?" I asked.

"Would you teach me to read and write?" he asked.

"You want me to teach you to read? That's what you want from me?" I said.

I could not hide my surprise. I started to laugh.

"I am not laughing at you. I am laughing at myself," I said. He let the situation fly right over his head; yet, there was a hint of a smile that suggested to him that what I had feared he might ask had not totally escaped him. This boy was different from most I had known. I hope he never changes. Well, I guess I hope that.

"Gramps taught me the ABC's, if that will help any," he said.

"He would have taught me to read, only he didn't know how himself. He worried over not being able to teach me some things," he said. "He was good at numbers though. Could you, or would you teach me?" he asked. His voice was almost pleading.

"You know," I said, "I don't even remember how I learned to read. But if you want to try, I will sure give it my best shot. Knowing your alphabet will help. Why don't you say it for me."

He went from A to Z without a hitch.

"Can you write or print the alphabet?" I asked.

"Not all of them," he said, "but I think I know the shape of most of them."

He smoothed out an area near the fire and with a stick started drawing the alphabet in the ash dust.

Thus began a nightly routine. After the chores were done, teacher and student worked and copied and worked some more. Birch bark became our paper and charcoal sticks the pencils. He eventually learned to draw, then print his name. It was rote memory at first, but then he actually began to write.

He was pleased when he had mastered his name.

It was like he had discovered his identity.

One evening he said, "I would like to sign my name to the partnership papers." I had forgotten that he had not signed. He couldn't have signed before but now he can.

He used my ballpoint pen. No one in the world has ever signed their name with more pride and care.

"This calls for a celebration," I said, "break out the popcorn or should I say pop seeds."

I was the eager teacher and he was a most eager student. He learned fast even with the crude instructional tools at hand. I decided to use the pilot's manual for his textbook. I would write three-or-four line short stories for him to read, and he copied them over and over.

We started leaving simple notes to each other when we went our separate ways. His might say something like, Down by crick—be back by 3. Now how in the hell would I know if it was three or whatever? He would laugh and remind me ,"You can read books but I can read the sun."

Every night, no matter what, he worked on his reading, writing, and spelling. When I was too tired or wanted to quit early he still continued on his own

He was bright, and I was encouraged by his progress to the point that what could have been a boring repetitive process became quite interesting.

Chapter 20

Merry Christmas

December 23 or 25

What is this?" I asked. He had his hand extended with what looked like a piece of fur and a piece of birch bark. The soft bark was folded in the middle. It opened to say, *Merry Christmas 1986* and on the second line it said, *From Donovan McDowell.*

I didn't even have to look at the gift to know that it was going to be the nicest Christmas present I had ever received and it was.

The gift was a beautiful, light brown hat with ear flaps that tied under my chin. It was a work of art. I had never felt such soft fur before. I didn't know what to say but I did manage to get out, "Thank you, it is so lovely. It feels like sable."

"Three muskrats," he said

"Thank you very much," I said. "I don't remember you saying that you had snared any muskrats. I am glad we didn't have to eat them." There was an uncomfortable pause. "We didn't eat them, did we?"

"No ,we haven't eaten them—yet," he replied.

"The fur will shed water," he said.

"I don't have a present for you," I said, "but I do

wish you a very Merry Christmas from the bottom of my heart. The gift was thoughtful and the card is a treasure."

"I can write you a Christmas card and sign my full name because of you," the Monkey said. "You have given me the best present in the world. You taught me to read and write."

I turned as though to adjust the hat, but I think he saw my tears .

We ate rabbit and camas stew with hazelnuts dipped in honey. It was a Christmas feast.

According to my diary it was December 23rd not the 25th, but I never mentioned it to him. How could we really know for sure what day this was? We could have lost track.

When I leave this place there will definitely be room somewhere in my pack for my Christmas card.

It snowed off and on the entire evening with a slight breeze. The only noise in that land was the crackle of the fire. We didn't have our school tonight. He went out to look around and then I went to bed.

So passes Christmas ,1986. "White Christmas" has a different meaning to me this year. Where will I be next Christmas? I wished I had some way to tell Mom not to worry.

Chapter 21

Through The Ice

January 20, 1987

New Year's Day came and went. It seemed strange to write 1987. The Monkey was somewhere downstream, probably picking up rocks to study. He did this wherever he went even though we had long since closed down the mining operation. The air was crisp. It hadn't snowed for several days, but there was a substantial build-up on the ground. I had completed my work for the day around the camp and I was restless. Fresh fish sounded good to me. The pond had been frozen over for weeks except for a small area right behind the main beaver lodge, and one area where the water flowed over the dam. The current in these two areas kept the pond from totally freezing over.

The Monkey had been successful in fishing off the dam into the small area of open water. I had watched The Monkey take an hour or more to pick his way across the top of the dam and then fish for about half an hour, and then pick his way back the next hour. It was a lot of time spent for so little fishing.

It was already mid-afternoon and this slow route wasn't going to get the job done today. My plan was to walk the easy part of the dam, then test the ice at that point. I was certain that the ice would hold my weight. From there I could walk the sixty feet or so toward the beaver lodge and fish in the open water behind the lodge. The Monkey had not fished there yet. It might produce some quick results.

The walk on the top of the dam took more time than I had thought. The sticks and mud that comprised the surface of the dam were frozen and slippery. I decided to test the ice before I left the comparative safety of the dam. It held. I bounced several times and it appeared solid, as I thought.

The walking across the ice proved faster than trying to maintain my footing on the top of the dam. Within five minutes of careful sliding, one foot ahead of the other, I had reached within about fifteen feet of the open water. The ice groaned a few times, but held fine.

With my second cast I already had a fish on. This was going to be great. The fish was of good size but not at all cooperative. It kept running under the ice shelf and I couldn't snatch it out onto the ice. I became concerned that the edge of the ice might cut my line.

I will never know exactly what happened next, but in any case the whole area of ice I was standing on suddenly tilted and broke off. I knew at once that I was in serious trouble. I went under the water. When I popped up to the surface I was in the open water behind the beaver lodge. I recall being surprised at how much current there was in the pond. The current was taking me toward the dam. Perhaps,

I thought, I could grab hold of something on the dam and pull myself out.

The current tried to drag me under the ice shelf. With great effort I raised my arms so that my elbows rode on the ice shelf. My legs and lower body were swept under the ice.

I had been in the water no more than two or three minutes, but already I had no feeling in my legs. I hurt so badly that I wondered if it might be better to let go. What would The Monkey do? I tried to shout but I could not make a sound come out. I had my whistle on the string around my neck, but to reach it I would have to let go with one hand and I was afraid to try. Who would hear me anyway? I tried to think but I couldn't seem to make anything work. At least I didn't hurt any more. A realization came over me that I was going to die. After all I had been through, I was not going to make it this time. I stopped trying to think, and became much calmer. Thoughts of my Mother came to me as clearly as if she were right beside me. She was trying to tell me something.

I suddenly realized someone was shouting. How could that be? It sounded so far away.

"Listen to me. Listen to me…"

Something about a stick and my legs.

"Listen to me." The Monkey was here.

What does he mean? What stick? I am so tired. I don't understand.

"Put the stick that is in front of you between your legs. Do it now."

Maybe I didn't hear it all. Then I thought I understood. He wanted me to take a short limb that he had somehow thrown in front of me and put it through my legs. But to do that I would have to take my elbows off the ice shelf. I couldn't do that. I couldn't bring myself to let go.

"Do it now. Put the stick behind your legs. Don't wait. Do it now."

Oh hell, what's the use? I wanted to tell him I was going to try to grab the stick with one hand.

"No, not with your hands. Put it between your legs. Please do what I say!"

I made one desperate effort with one hand but still kept my other hand on the ice shelf. Maybe he would stop shouting at me if I tried once. I managed to get the stick through my crotch and for the first time realized that he had a the cord attached to the stick. But the ice shelf broke again and I went under. Almost at once I could feel the tug on the stick which was behind my legs now and I popped out on top of the ice.

It seemed like an eternity while he pulled me steadily across the ice toward the shore. I tried to reach out with my hands to take the cord and straighten my direction but I could not tell if my hands were open or closed.

I have no idea how he got me to the cave, but it must have been some job. I can vaguely remember him trying to pour some of his awful tea brew in my mouth, but I couldn't swallow.

I woke up shivering in uncontrolled spasms that shook my whole body. I must be alive. *Otherwise why would I hurt so much?* It was very dark but The Monkey had a huge fire going. I could see him working around the fire. At first I couldn't focus on what he was doing. Apparently he had wrapped warmed rocks in layers of rabbit skins and material and shoved them inside my sleeping bag. He had me stuffed deep into the sack and I could not see him very well. I did not let on yet that I had rejoined the living. I was just too tired and still couldn't stop shaking. I was surprised at how dry I seemed to be. I could see him a little better now. He looked like he had been crying. He must have gotten a serious injury this time because as far as I knew he had not cried a tear with his broken leg.

When the last two rocks were in place I got a big surprise. He slipped off his pants and shirt and crawled in beside me. He put the last two warm rocks in the pit of my stomach and held them in place with his own nearly naked body. It was then that I realized that I had only the survival blanket wrapped around me in the sleeping bag.

His arms seemed to encircle me about four times, at least, and somehow he still had a hand free to keep rubbing my back and neck. I felt safe and at peace and dozed off again.

I awoke several times in the night. One time he was trying to get some warm water or broth or something down me. Several times I was aware of a new supply of warm rocks being placed in the sleeping bag and against my stomach. Once he slipped in behind me in the sleeping bag but he couldn't get the rocks to hold in place, so he changed to the front again. I had not uttered a word now for many hours. I could have said something, but I just didn't.

I slept most of the time but I was aware that day had come and gone and it was dark again. All that night and through the next day he kept up the warm rock routine and on occasion he tried to get warm liquid down me. I think he did get me to take some liquid.

I was awake again. It was now mid-day. I was still drowsy but I knew I was going to live. I had been awake for some time but did not move. The Monkey was wrapped around me and had dozed off to sleep. He felt so warm and comfortable next to me that on an impulse I moved the rock between us to one side and pulled myself closer to him.

I thought that if ever I was able to talk again I would tell him that this wasn't such a bad idea. He still slept. I slid my body fully up against his. His eyes popped open and stared into mine for what seemed like a very long time. I pressed a little harder to him.

"I think you are warm enough," he said. He quickly extracted himself from me.

"I'm sorry if I frightened you," I said. I could barely speak above a whisper. "Don't be embarrassed," I said.

He was silent but he got into his clothes so fast it was almost comical.

Later, I slowly put on my clothes, which were all dried out and warmed by the fire. The fire still blazed high.

"Here is some meat broth I want you to try," he said, "it will be good for you. I have not been able to get much down you."

He was all business. I cupped my hands around the container and began to sip slowly. It did taste good. I then made the mistake of pursuing the earlier incident a bit more.

"You haven't been around girls much have you?" I asked. I repeated my question because I didn't think he understood me.

"I heard you the first time," he said. "No, I haven't been around girls at all. I have thought some about them, sure, but right now our job is to think about living through this winter. If we do make it out, there will be plenty enough time then for you to think about boys, and for me to think about girls."

I knew this remarkable guy meant it and I also knew just as well that he was going to make sure that a similar situation was not going to ever happen again.

"I owe you my life," I said. My voice was barely audible.

"I know," he said. His voice was equally low. "Better try to get some more sleep now," he said.

Chapter 22

Factors to Combat

February 18

The winter wore on and on with very little to break the monotony. There was always work to be done, but it was so repetitive, just like the day before and the day before that. We were never at the point of starving, but we never had quite enough to eat. Camas became our mainstay food. Fresh meat was harder and harder to come by. If we had one successful snare a week we were fortunate. We seldom even had our snares tripped. You can't eat a tripped snare but it does keep you encouraged to know that some game at least found your trap interesting.

"Either the game is more scarce or a lot smarter," The Monkey said.

The lack of success in snaring frustrated me, but to The Monkey it only increased his level of respect for the creatures of the wild. At times I got the impression that he was actually not too disappointed when the snares were empty.

"The animals have changed their habits and we have not adjusted," he said.

What meat we had was what we had cured last fall. It was fortunate that the Monkey had insisted that we store the meat in small separate batches, because over half of the meat spoiled. Some meat just cures better I guess. I felt relieved, frankly, that the muskrat meat did not keep. The hazelnuts were gone but the acorns were still in good supply.

The snow was very deep. It was hip deep on the level, but in places where the wind had caused drifts, it was twenty feet deep right next to practically bare ground.

Wood had become a major worry to us. A great deal of our stored wood was consumed when the Monkey kept such a big fire going night and day, while I was recovering from my swim under the ice.

It is a paradox to be short of fuel in a virgin forest. We have to cut "green" wood now. The heat value is so reduced that the work would be questionable, except for the fact that poor returns is a lot better than no returns.

There was one change in our routine. The Monkey sent me out to scrounge for rose hips.

"What is a rose hip," I asked, "and what do we do with them?"

"You would call the 'hip' a bud," he said. "You know, a rose bud. And we eat them."

"And we eat them? We are down to eating rose buds?" I said.

The rose hip is the tiny bud of the wild rose. It is only about a quarter of an inch in diameter. They hang on the bushes all winter and the deer just love them. The Monkey claimed the rose hip is loaded with the same vitamins as citrus fruit. If that were true, it would be vitamin C, of course. He claimed the British gathered rose hips in World War Two when England could not get citrus fruits. It was a good story anyway.

We took the buds and smashed them up, and mixed them with honey because they are very bitter. We started taking a dose of the junk every day.

Each day wore on, not much different from the day before. The Monkey still got up before daybreak, but I found myself staying in my sleeping bag longer each day. At least I was warm in bed. I would have been glad to get up if there were really anything to do. *How many rose hips can you gather? Monotony and boredom are becoming real factors to combat.*

The only part of our day that was going well and gave me something to look forward to was the reading lessons. The Monkey was doing very well. I was sure it was my natural skills as a teacher. I wouldn't describe him as exactly being fluent yet, but he was beyond mere word recognition. *Isn't that something— when the most exciting thing of the day is to teach this kid to read? Oh well.*

I think The Monkey sensed that boredom could become a negative and dangerous factor. He was starting to go over our "escape" plans with me to get me more involved.

"Our departure will not be a matter of getting up some morning to say 'look the weather is fine. Let's be on our way, '" he said.

"I never thought it would be that simple," I said.

"Survival in a stationary camp is a lot easier than trying to live in a nomadic situation," he said. "For an unknown length of time we will be nomads. Everything we use we will have to carry with us. Every camp will be out in the open..."

"OK, OK, I can see there will be a major difference," I said.

"I've been doing a little thinking..." he said.

"Let's hear it. I know there is a plan cooking in your head." I said. He had a plan, and it was something in which I could participate. He had cooked up something to break the monotony which was his real purpose, I am convinced of that. The 'escape' plan became almost incidental Even a good argument over an aspect of the plan was welcome.

"To solve the problem of camping on the move, I propose a series of camps to be established ahead of time," he said.

Well, it was a plan. At least we were working on something.

"I think about five camps set up about five to ten miles apart, depending upon the terrain, and so forth," he said. "That should get us about half-way to the coast. I hope."

"I now know that you expect us to hike between five and ten miles each day. It would seem to me that we could go a little faster than that. I have walked twenty miles in the March of Dimes walk-a-thons," I said.

"The what? Twenty miles is too much to have time to set up camp in daylight. The only way we could do twenty, would be to lay over the next day, so you would be averaging the same distance anyway. But tell me more about these marches," he said.

"Let's talk more about the camps you want to set up. The marches don't have much to do with this," I decided.

Some of this planning is time-consuming nonsense. He involves me in some of it just to keep my mind occupied. He has made up his mind on some things that don't appear to be open for discussion. Some of his stubbornness is over very trivial matters. A classic example of this, is his insistence on naming these camps, that are not even set up yet. I think it would be logical to just number the camps. Camp number one, camp number two, and so on. He wants to name each of them after characters out of Irish history. Who gives a damn what we name them? I just think it will be confusing his way. He wants to argue about this all the time.

"If we have to name the camps rather than just number them," I said, "why not name them after famous women?" That got him sputtering.

At least the planning, and even the silly arguments, took my mind off the deadly boring daily routine.

Chapter 23

Spring Blizzard

March 16

A few signs of spring are apparent. However, the winter is not quite over. The pond is still frozen over but the precipitation that falls is as likely to be rain as snow. That is a good sign. It is warming up.

We had our first 'trail camp' set up. It was, only four miles down the valley. Not as far as we would have liked the first camp to be, but it was far enough for now with the many drifts of snow still to negotiate. I called this 'Camp Number One' but the Monkey christened it 'Camp Brendan' after some Irish Saint who was a famous navigator or explorer.

"Perhaps you don't realize that St. Brendan was the first explorer from the Old World to reach North America," he said.

"You are right on that one," I said, "I didn't know that, and I bet Columbus didn't know it either. Nor for that matter, is any historian likely aware of it. We must be sure to correct all the history books at our first opportunity."

There was only a slight downhill grade to Camp One. In other words we do not reduce our elevation very much, which means the first camp does not get us down the mountain far enough to get out of the soft snow. We laid in an ample supply of wood which was easy to scrounge because of all the blowdown in the area. Each time we left Camp Brendan we set up the next fire and covered it with our well-worn tarp, which we got from the survival kit, so that when we return to bring the next load of supplies all we'll have to do is peel the tarp off and we'll have a fire going in minutes.

Our temporary shelter at the camp was a pole lean-to laid up against a fallen log. It was very much like the first shelter the Monkey had me make soon after the crash.

"We will carry as many supplies as we can each time," he said. "When the snow melts we will leap-frog these supplies to the next trail camp we set up, and so on, until we have a string of trail camps all ready for us. Each camp will be about a day's hike from the last one. When we finally leave the cave for good there won't be much to pack. Our gear will be strung out on the trail."

"I hope this doesn't prove to be a mistake," I said.

The evenings were busier than ever. Extra foot socks were being made, only with shorter tops.

"Weight is a major factor in any hike plan," he said, "even to the point of making our boot socks shorter."

He made list after list refining what we wanted at Camp Five as opposed to Camp Three or One, and so on.

"You would think we were planning a military campaign," I said.

"It has many of the same features," he said, " Getting supplies to the troops at the right time is every general's worry."

But the most remarkable aspect was the fact that he could write all these lists down. He had a piece of birch bark labeled for each of the proposed camps. He could transfer items from one camp list to another with ease.

The winter still held on so we did not try to push on to make the second trail camp.

"Don't worry, the winter will break soon, and when it does everything will fall in place for us," he said.

"I hope you are right. This snow is getting old," I said.

I think we are living too much off our limited stores. I feel we should take some time to replenish our supplies even though the game is still scarce. Perhaps we will re-stock just before we leave.

I have been reminded by the Monkey that today is March 17th, St. Patrick's day. I couldn't care less. What does matter however, is the looks of the sky and the falling temperature. The Monkey is concerned too. He casually suggested that we not take the next load to the trail camp today as we had planned to do.

By mid-morning it was snowing hard and the wind was whipping up in strong gusts. Our pennant weather vane stood straight out, showing the direction of the wind to be generally from the north-west.

"It looks like winter is going to take one more stand against us," he said." Spring storms are sometimes the worst."

"When does a spring storm become a spring blizzard?" I asked.

"About two hours ago," he said.

March 18

The visibility was so bad now that I did not venture out today at all. The Monkey went out only as far as the wood storage area, which was just around the rock wall of the cave. His last armload of wood was small, and with concern in his voice he said, "That's it. Our wood supply next door is gone, used up."

"We still have bark that we stored inside the cave," I said.

"I know," he said. "Unfortunately, we have used the bark too often for our morning fires rather than going to the wood pile outside. The net result is, we are low on fuel. Something had better happen soon."

Did I pick up a hint of panic in his voice? Just a hint?

The heaviest snowfall of the year was occurring right now.

March 20

This was the fourth day of blizzard conditions, and confinement was taking its toll. We slept very little because we were keeping as small a fire as we could We just stayed huddled over the fire. I don't see how we could have slept much anyway because of the howling winds.

For the first time in a long time sharp words were exchanged between us. I started it, I guess, with an uncalled-for remark.

"If we had spent those weeks that you played

49er getting wood and food, we probably wouldn't be in this fix," I said.

His reply, to my admittedly stupid comment, was a real shocker to me.

"I didn't fall through the ice. I didn't have to be told every little thing that needed to be done time after time. You have not pulled your weight since we have been here," the Monkey said.

Not another word was spoken between us that evening. Great damage had been done and I didn't know any way to repair it.

March 21

This morning (our fifth day of the storm I think) The Monkey made an alarming announcement. "We must make our final effort soon," he said.

"Final?"

"We cannot wait until we run completely out of food and wood," he said, "if we don't replenish our supplies now we will weaken too fast, and we will not be able to do anything about our situation. Too often people wait too long."

At least we were talking again. It wasn't hard to inventory our supplies. The wood and bark were gone. A bed of coals was all that remained. The last of the acorns had been eaten the day before. That was it. We were out.

"We have some food at Camp Brendan," I said. "Is it time to make a try for it?"

"No, I don't think so," he said. "Even if we could find our way to the camp, which is doubtful, we only have three or four pounds of food cached there. We will use up more energy to get there than we would gain from the food. Besides, I'm not so much worried about starving as I am about freezing to death. We do still have possibilities for food."

"Like what?" I said.

"Like our belts," he said, "like any of the skins we have".

He had thought this over. His answer came too quickly.

"No, it is not food, it is fuel. Wood is our top priority," he said, "and it has to be today. It has to be now."

That was not going to be easy. We were still in a virtual whiteout. I have no idea what the temperature was except to say that ice has formed on the inside of the cave walls. That had not happened until now. I don't even want to think about the wind-chill factor.

"We will need fuel for one more hot fire," he said, "what ever new fuel we get will be green and wet. It will take a lot of heat to dry it out to the point that it will burn."

I knew he was coming up with a plan, but whatever the plan might consist of, it would mean going outside the cave. I didn't want to think about that.

"We can split up the one-legged stools and the stump chairs. Plus, we can burn the cedar sleeping mats and our cedar rain gear," the Monkey said. "This won't burn long but it will burn hot," he said.

I didn't like this plan, but I didn't have a better one. He was not going to have us sit by and let us freeze without a good fight. I was going to suggest that we wait until morning— but day or night, the visibility was about the same, so I remained quiet. I watched as he split up the stools and the stump chairs. I gathered the cedar bark rain gear, the mats, and the braided cedar ropes and deposited it all in a pile. He looked over the pile and removed the cedar rope.

"Here is the plan," he said. " We tie together everything we have that could serve as a rope. We tie the ends of our rope together to form a continuous loop. I will go out with the bow saw with the loop around my waist. The first tree I come to, I will cut off limbs and tie the limbs to the rope. You pull the rope in and untie the load. I will always keep the loop around my waist so I won't get lost out there. How does the plan sound to you?"

What could I say? "I think it will work," I said "but do you think you will be able to walk against that wind?"

"Stand? If I make it at all it will be by crawling on all fours," he said.

I do feel better knowing that we have a plan, but I have no idea if it will work or not. After days of doing little or nothing, not even talking, we are working together again.

With the-nylon cord, and strings of electrical wire from the plane spliced together, plus the braided cedar rope, we ended up with a 'rope' about two hundred and fifty feet long. Tied in a loop it cut our range in half. So the Monkey would have a range of only one hundred and twenty-five feet from the mouth of the cave. In one respect that didn't seem very far, but on the other hand it was a long way from any protection from the wind and cold. With no visibility and under these conditions this could be the distance of his life. We both knew that.

The opening to the cave was blocked with snow frozen into ice. It took nearly two hours, I guess, to cut and shovel a trench through the doorway just to get out. He wanted the opening to be level with the floor of the cave so that I would not have to pull up-hill right at the entrance.

"I have a lot of concern over the strength of the cedar rope portion," he said.

He tried to shout his final instructions from the opening, but his words were lost in the wind. The instructions were important so he waved me back to the fire pit where he could be heard. The fire was only coals, but he hovered over them as though he were trying to sponge up all the heat he could while he talked.

"Two tugs on the rope means to pull in, one tug means to stop. If I pull three times it means I'm in trouble. Tie down your end and follow the rope and come get me. Don't leave the cave except to get me. If I don't cone back, and if you don't feel the three tugs on the rope, don't leave the cave because all you would be bringing back would be a block of ice. Don't let me pull the rope all the way out no matter what."

I nodded that I understood. He had more to say.

"If the rope breaks don't pull it in," he said. "Do you understand? Don't pull the rope in."

I nodded.

"You will be pulling in wet limbs and maybe some bark, but it will all be wet or green or both. Don't put it on the fire until I get back. We don't want to smother the fire with wet stuff."

"My plan is to go straight out from the opening of the cave, so you should have a straight pull. Pull it softly. I will tie the limbs on so they should slide on the snow. But don't horse it too much. It will be small loads. We can't afford to break the rope."

The thin collection of spliced together strands had become more than a rope to me, it was our lifeline.

When he rolled over the top he looked like a pregnant raccoon. The only thing visible were his eyes. He had double-socked his shoes, he had two pairs of mittens crammed on, and his skull cap was on under his tie-down fur hat. He wrapped skins around his neck and face.

I tried to send him off with some humor by shouting, "Now you come straight home from work." My words were lost to a blast of wind. With the bow saw over his shoulder and the rope around his waist he was soon gone from sight.

It took forever, it seemed, to play out the rope. but at last it stopped. I knew he had found his first tree. *It is strange that here we are in the center of a forest and he is out there somewhere "feeling" for a tree.* It could not be just any tree however, it had to be a tree with limbs he could reach in order to saw them.

It was an eternity before I felt two distinct tugs on the rope. The first 'catch' was on the line. A slow steady pull finally produced a Douglas fir bough four feet long and about two inches in diameter. Then came a bare limb stripped of its needles. It was also about four feet long but larger in diameter. I tried to visualize his efforts and what must be going on at his end of the rope. He was obviously working on a Douglas fir and was cutting off pieces of a limb from the end of the bough to the trunk of the tree. This would account for each cut being progressively larger in diameter. My guess was that he had found the tree that he called "the wolf tree," with many boughs going all the way to the ground. I knew whenever he moved to a new limb by the arrival of a bough with all the short limbs and needles still on it. It would take forever this way, I thought. However, I was surprised at what two hours of work produced. I never thought he would be able to stay out in the storm for any length of time, with the chill factor level at what it must have been, but he did.

At last, I could tell by the action on the rope that he had tied it off and was coming in, following the rope.

I had a bowl of water on the coals that had reached lukewarm. He could pretend it was soup or broth or anything he wished. He appreciated it.

"Green wood can be burned pretty effectively," he said in between shivers. "The key is to have a hot fire to start with." With that the death knell of the stools, chairs, and cedar rain gear was sounded.

He cut the green limbs into logs about two feet long. He inserted just the tips of each green log into the fire. As the fire burned the tips became dry, and combusted. We kept slowly feeding the green logs into the main part of the fire. The green limbs were being dried just before they burned.

For the first time in a week we were going to sleep warm. The fire was not huge, but at this point nothing ever looked or felt better.

The fire meant more than warmth to two half-frozen people. It meant a resurgence of hope and a return of our determination to live.

"When this storm lulls, and it will, we will get all the snares we can muster into operation," he said. "All the animals in the valley will be out scouting for food, and so will we."

I knew we would be O.K. now. He was working on our next plan.

Chapter 24

The Big River

April 10

It was spring. No false spring this time. We knew that winter was over. You cannot imagine the uplifting of spirits that came over us. There was now plenty of game, and we ate fresh meat every day. We broke the last shelf of ice on the beaver pond, and it was a fisherman's delight.

The blue jays, which we had not seen nor heard from for nearly two months, started scolding us again just as if they had never stopped.

The thing that amazes me the most is the profusion of little wildflowers that bloom wherever the ground is bare of snow. It is not uncommon for the flowers to bloom right through the trailing edge of a snowdrift.

Perky yellow flowers, which I learned were called buttercups and dainty little blue Johnie-Jump-Ups were everywhere.

The saga of our Canada geese has a happy ending. Every day huge flocks of geese flew overhead going north. Just as in the fall, our geese could hear their friends long before we could. As the flocks passed over there would be a great commotion and squawking back and forth.

"I don't see how they made it through the winter," he said. "I expected the injured hen to have been fox food," the Monkey said.

Four or five times a day our pair of geese would fly from one end of the pond to the other. At times they rose high above the valley floor.

"She is strong enough to fly away," he said. "I don't know why they don't join one of the flocks going north."

The answer was soon in coming. About fifty geese broke off from a big wedge going over and dropped down on our pond. Talk about a homecoming. It had to be the same flock of geese that reluctantly left our geese last fall. Our geese were just waiting for the right flock. They had known all along they would be picked up by their friends. They knew they would not be forgotten.

The geese spent the afternoon and evening with us and left at daybreak. It sounds incredible, but the whole valley quieted down for the lift-off. Even the blue jays seemed to pay silent tribute. The Monkey ran and got the flares from the survival kit. It was to be our version of a twenty-one-gun salute. The damn thing didn't work. But we cheered and clapped as the flock with our two geese in it cleared the trees.

The valley was alive and on the move. *It is wonderful to be here. The creek has doubled in size as the snow melts at the higher elevations.* The run-off slowed down our fishing. The water was milky white for the most part of the day and the fish wouldn't bite. Late in the afternoons the creek cleared up for a short time, and that was the only time we could fish.

"The clearing of the water each day is caused by the cooling down of the runoff high in the mountains," he explained.

The delta where we did our mining is now a river running about hip deep. We are anxious to see how we will find our trail camp and the gear we left there. We will have to wait for the creek to go down before we can cross it to get on the trail.

"We will go slower this time," the Monkey said. "We have all summer to make it out."

May 15, 1987

We reestablished Camp Number One, or Camp Brendan, as the Monkey still called it, and we established the second camp, or Camp Parnell. The distance between the two trail camps was probably eight miles. We could usually make the round trip in a day and a half by laying over at Camp Brendan on the return trip. We could come into the trail camps at dusk because we had already laid the fire before we left the previous day. We can have a fire going within minutes.

The trail we followed is a game trail which hangs on a flank of a hogback down the length of the valley. The trail was spectacular. It defies description. We meandered through gigantic old-growth fir and Sitka spruce with a floor like a carpet. We were never beyond the sound of the creek which supplied background music. We could always tell right where we were on the trail by the different sounds from the creek.

"This is some life," I said, "People pay thousands of dollars to go on a camping trip like this and we get it all for nothing."

Two miles beyond Camp Parnell the game trail turned at right angles to the creek. The reason for this was that the creek plunged into a rift in the mountains, forming a narrow canyon only yards wide. The sides of the chasm were made of solid rock over a hundred feet to the creek below. The creek at this point was flowing north anyway, and we needed to turn west at some point. This seemed to be that place.

We climbed out onto a rock outcropping so we could survey a broad basin below us. It was a breath-taking sight.

"In the bottom of that big valley there is going to be one whale of a river," he said, "assuming that each of those converging gaps has a creek or a river in it the size of ours or larger." The Monkey pointed to the center of the U-shaped basin where the river must be. We could only imagine the size because we could not see it. All we could see was a blue green old-growth carpet which looked very smooth, but we knew it was not.

"That is where we are going, Sis," he said. "That river is our highway home. But we can't go in a direct line. We will go back and get on the game trail again. I would bet it will parallel the river below until there is a gap or a pass that will make our descent to the valley floor easier."

" It really looks like we could go for it right from

here," I said.

"If we were crows I would agree with you, but since we are not, we will take the same route that the game has been taking since the beginning of time."

By the end of the next week we had Camp Wolfe-Tone established, about four miles west of Camp Parnell. The going slowed down because the Monkey insisted upon blazing trees to mark the trail. *I guess it is something you do, but it certainly takes more time.*

Another five miles and we set up Camp Four. (Camp O'Connell to the Monkey.) He's not out of Irish heroes yet. From Camp O'Connell the game trail turned directly and suddenly toward the river. We had been gradually going downhill for several miles but at this point the trail went direct.

"This is the pass we have been looking for," he said. "Our next camp will be our last and it will be somewhere on that river."

"The Big River," I said. "Until we find out the real name for the river, let's call it the Big River," I said.

"Fine, the Big River it is," he said.

"How about that. I thought for sure we would have to call it the Shannon or the Liffey," I said.

On the south shore of the Big River we established our fifth and last trail camp. The Monkey dubbed this one Camp Kennedy.

"Are you sure you want to call it Camp Kennedy?" I asked. "Kennedy didn't end up so well," I said.

"None of them ended well. They were Irish you

know," he said.

From the crest of the pass near Camp Four we could look into the distant west. What we saw was the Big River valley cutting range after range of mountains.

"We are farther away than we thought from the ocean aren't we?" I said.

"It looks that way. " he said. "It is possible, however, that we are looking over the top of a body of water to ridges and mountains on an island,"he added.

"We will build a makeshift raft here at Camp Kennedy," he said. "It won't have to be fancy because it will be the first of several we will be building. The water is slow enough in The Big River at Camp Kennedy to make and launch a raft—but we have no idea what lies downstream. At the first sign of an acceleration of the water, we will beach the raft and hoof it until the water is slow enough to take a raft again. We will then stop and build another raft. It will be your job to keep estimating our forward speed. I will show you an easy way to do that. Then the first sign that we're gaining speed, I want to know about it."

"That is exactly how Mark Twain got his start," I said.

"I don't know him, but it is an important job," he said. "We will drift as many miles on the river as we can in safety," he said.

We had worked our heavier gear up the trail camp by camp until most of it was at Camp Kennedy. We had to make only the final traverse from the cave to each camp, and then we would really be on our way. *It is the last of June and I am getting anxious for us to leave.*

Chapter 25

Deception

July 3

July 3rd, by my recollection our 298th day.

"We are as ready as we can be," the Monkey said.

"I think you have covered all the bases," I said, "tomorrow is the Fourth of July. Can we celebrate the fourth by leaving?"

"At the crack of dawn," he said, "as for covering all the bases it still depends on how good an idea it is to try to drift down an unknown river."

We had our final disagreement at the cave. I had prepared a little rock grotto to hold my diary. I located the grotto in a place where it would be noticeable. Well, the Monkey noticed it that is for sure and he seemed surprised.

"Are you going to leave your log?" he asked.

"I thought I would. Why not?" I said.

"Then you are not confident we will make it out, are you?" he said.

"No, it's not that," I said. "I haven't thought that we wouldn't get out. I just feel I should leave it. But yes, I have thought that there would be a chance that we would not make it. Maybe it is in the back of my mind. Don't tell me that you haven't had some doubts. I know I just want to make a little shrine so the diary might be found some day."

There was a very long silence, but I knew the conversation was not over. Something was bothering him.

"Of a practical matter,"he said finally, "may I ask if you have written anything about our finding gold?"

So that is what the problem is.

"Yes I did," I said.

"How much did you have to say?" he asked.

"I detailed it as much as I could," I said. "Here, you can read now. Do you want to read the whole damn diary?" He was taken aback. "No, I wouldn't do that," he said. "You know me better than that. What you have written down is your business,and where you leave it is your business, except for any mention about the gold. That becomes part of *my* business. And yes, I can read, and darn good too, thanks to you. But telling about the gold is something you should think about more." He was serious.

"Say more then," I said. I was just as serious.

" OK, let me give you just one example," he said. "Just suppose that an hour after we leave here, or the next day, someone arrives. It may sound silly after waiting months for a rescue party, to think that someone could show up, but ..."

"Silly is not the word for it," I said. "I can just hear someone say, 'Are you ready to be rescued now?' or, 'Could you tell us the best way to get to Denver? We took the wrong turn'."

"But, it could happen—especially as the weather warms up," he said. "They would read your log and say, 'Hey, they got gold on them. Well now isn't that interesting?' Finding our trail wouldn't be that hard. We have never tried to hide our trail or our camps. I would not be surprised if they circle ahead of us, eat our food, and wait for us to walk right into their arms. That way they wouldn't even have to carry the gold themselves."

He rattled this paranoid scenario off in rapid fashion. I was tempted to compare his tone to our blue jays, but I thought better of it. He had told me gold can change your personality, and once again, this was a classic case of that happening.

"You don't really believe all that crap do you?" I said.

Hey, when it comes to gold, men will kill for a speck of it, and we have more than a speck," he said. "As long as you have gold on you, your life is at risk, and don't you ever forget it. If you have any hint of the location of our diggings in that book, and it is found, the diary will never get back to your family."

Now that was the first thing he said that had a ring of truth to it.

The book will end up in someone's pack until they can claim the whole area," he said. "Somebody will use your own words to 'prove' their discovery."

"You have gone over the edge," I said. "The diary is mine."

"No. Any comments in the book about gold must come out," he said, "Don't even hint of gold. Look Sis, I mean it."

"Golly, you're getting all excited,"I said. "OK, OK, I will tear the pages out where I discuss anything about gold, and take it with me. Then I can replace the pages if the book is ever found—after I get it back, I mean."

"No good," he said. "You haven't been listening to me at all. To carry gold on us is bad enough but to carry information that tells where more can be found is dumb to the point of being reckless. I tell you it is packing your death sentence. I don't need the worry of watching our backs—and we don't have the time nor the energy to hide our trail."

I made one last appeal. "We could cover our first camp or the second one, and then we couldn't be followed."

"You don't understand," he said. "To hide our trail would mean having to set up false trails with double-back routes, no fires, and on and one. If I had thought we would be doing all of that I would not have blazed both sides of the trees on the trails I blazed the back side of each tree because I want to come back some day, or at least have it possible to come back. For *us* to come back I mean."

"For *us*? For *us* to return? Now that was an after thought if I ever heard one," I said.

He stood close over me menacingly where I was sitting.

"I am not fooling around," he said.

I should have kicked his butt around months ago when I had the chance. The thought crossed my mind that this might still be a good time to do it but looking up into his eyes, I suddenly had second thoughts about the wisdom of trying that.

"O.K., back off," I said. "Give me a little time. I will purge the diary."

If this is found and if you have read this far you know that I did not do what I said I would. I did tear out some pages with writing on them. I have blank pages that I thought about tearing out to burn, but I thought that he might go over and stir the ashes and be able to determine some way that I only burned blank pages. Then there would be another scene, and he might insist upon reading the whole diary. He could read it too, thanks to the many, many hours I spent teaching that turkey how to read.

The pages I tore out were descriptions of wild-flowers, getting the honey out of the bee tree, and some corny stuff about my appreciation for the Monkey for what he did during the ice situation. I did change some critical words and scratched out some specifics about where we did our digging. Someone will be able to figure it all out eventually, I know, but at least it is not just handed to them. They will have to do something on their own.

I sat by the fire and burned page by page, and wouldn't you know it, he did stir up the ashes. The Monkey had reverted to the training of extreme caution when it came to gold taught to him by his Grandfather. *I wonder if they really trusted each other when they panned together. I bet the old man held out on him at times.*

Enough of this morbid interlude. I hope I can see the expression on the Monkey's face if he ever finds out that I didn't purge the diary.

Chapter 26

Departure

July 4 - Independence Day

We made our final arrangements so that we could leave at the crack of dawn. I didn't see the need to leave that early since we would be at Camp Brendan by midday, but that was the plan. The Monkey cut extra wood and stacked it by the fire pit. In the morning we planned to water down the fire, our last fire and lay tinder so that it will only require a match to touch it off. I wished we had had it that easy all those months ago. He even left my spent lighter on top of the pile of wood. The lighter had been out of fluid for months but the flint striker could still be used if someone had the intelligence to do so. I wouldn't have had the smarts when I first got here.

He coated the saw blade with the last of the beeswax and hung the saw on the wall of the cave along with the steel snares. We didn't leave a scrap of food,however.

We did not have much to carry because all the heavier items like the axe were stored ahead of us in the trail camps. *The Monkey has his "stuff" in a leather tube tied around his waist. My "stuff" is in a leather pouch in my pack. If we run into trouble on the raft segment of the trip I want to be able to shed the weight of the "stuff." The Monkey will have a little more trouble if the raft upsets.*

I will make my last entry in my diary in the morning before we leave, but there is one more entry to make tonight. The Monkey is asleep now and I was already in the sack too, but I can't sleep now so I am writing by the last light from the fire.

We turned in early because we were dead tired, and tomorrow will be a big day. The Monkey called to me.

"Sis, will you hear my prayers tonight?" he asked.

I was surprised. "Did you ask your Grandfather to listen to your prayers on special occasions?" I asked.

"No, never", he said.

"Sure—if you want me to," I said. "I can just listen from over here can't I?" I said.

"Sure. Thank you." There was a long pause, to gather his thoughts, I suppose.

"Dear Lord, if it be Thy will, watch us on the way out. Keep us from any falls or missteps. Don't let us get lost."

That was the first I had heard of any concerns about getting lost.

"Thank you for giving me Sis to stay with. She is the only friend I have ever had."

My God, could that be true?

"Thank you for giving her the patience to overlook my ignorance, and then to do something about it. Gramps, if you are listening, you know how hard I tried to remember what you taught me. I miss you so. Stay with us all the way out. And if it be Thy will, have Sis's mom and friends be as happy to see her as she will be to see them. Amen."

They will all be happy to see me. I know my family and friends will be happy when they hear that I have returned safe and sound. I have gone over my homecoming a thousand times in my mind.

Who would be there to meet the Monkey? There was no one waiting for news from him. How sad. My arrival 'out' meant something to me. What does it mean to the Monkey? *The truth is he doesn't know what it will mean.*

I was struck by how much of his prayer was about me and how little was about himself. I was glad he went right to sleep. He did not hear me blowing my nose or see me wiping my eyes. But now I really can't sleep.

* * * * * * * * * * * * * * * * *

The sun crawled above the rim of the valley, the place we had called home for the last ten months or so. It was chilly, but we know it would be a beautiful day.

The Monkey was already across the creek and had started up the bank when he turned around to see what my delay was. I waved him on and signed to him that I would catch up with him on the trail. He motioned he understood. I watched him climb the incline to the trail. I could see him on the trail for a short distance before he was gone out of sight into the timber. He never looked back at the valley. Not even a glance.

I heard the blue jays scold me for the last time. Their disposition had not improved. The stillness of the pond was broken by the top of a head and then the eyes of a beaver. The familiar slap of the beaver's tail indicated that it knew it had been spotted, so now all the beavers in beaver-land were warned.

This is such a beautiful spot. So peaceful and quiet. But not so quiet if you know what to listen for. I have learned to listen. I have learned so much.

I crossed the creek, climbed the bank and sat down, just to sponge in every sight and sound that I could. I could see the mound of stones with the cross tied together with wire. I could see the faded orange signal flag hanging limp from the slender alder tree in the stillness. The new leaves made the signal flag hard to see. *We will have to move it to a better location.* That thought brought a smile.

I could see the old wolf tree with the branches sawed off on one side, and I thought about the blizzard. The Monkey went by at least four trees that would have been closer, but that night, in that storm, how could he have known.

The plane was nearly covered by new growth. It will never be spotted from the air. *I hope the doe and her twin fawns would come for another drink under the oak tree. We have seen the deer family several times this spring.* We were so happy that they had made it through the winter. But the deer did not wish to make a farewell visit, I guess.

My thoughts were interrupted by the sudden squawking and flapping of the kingfisher. "O.K. my friend, the last word is yours."

I returned to my little rock shrine to deposit these last few pages which I will put in the back of the diary loose.

"That is it. I'm out of here. Gramps McDowell, please walk with us."

Epilogue

A few weeks after our hunting trip, I delivered the diary to the address in Seattle, Washington, as the author of the diary had requested.

I had anticipated the thrill of handing the diary to Miss Susan Simpson, in person. However, I had to be satisfied with turning over the diary to Mrs. Simpson, Susan's often mentioned and beloved mother.

Susan Simpson and Donovan(Monkey) McDowell did not make it out to civilization in the spring of 1987.

Their fate is unknown.

The End

Whiskey Riley

There is a mystique surrounding the men who work underground, where trust and loyalty, honor, and death are not abstract and where humor often compensates for fear. The tunnels have vanished under hundreds of feet of water, the men to the next job—neither to be seen again.

The novel *Whiskey Riley* recaptures this subculture in a factually base story of the drilling of the tunnels at Yale Dam on the Lewis River in Southwest Washington.

ORDER FORM

Name_____

Address_____

City, State, Zip _____

Phone_____

Enclosed is my check for $16.95 ($14.95 + $ 2.00 shipping and handling.)

for *FOLLOW THE RIVER*

or *WHISKEY RILEY,*
the author's other novel.

Esjay Press

4310 Shoreline Drive N.
Keizer, Oregon 97303-5831

Phone 1-503-390-2519 for orders or
INTERNET: mcgee_ jerry@msn.com

NOTE: Please indicate if you want it autographed
and to whom.